He stumbled into the club where she sang,
and her life was never the same again . . .

Esther Hoffman was singing her heart out at The Old Place when John Norman staggered in drunk, a bottle of vodka in his hand. He was a famous rock star, and pretty soon people were watching him instead of listening to her.

Of course, he became the center of a brawl. Everywhere he went trouble erupted. But he took Esther with him as he sped away from the riot. Her voice, her honesty and her spirit reached him through the haze of drink and pills. It was the beginning of a career for Esther and the start of a love affair for both of them—an affair that held both promise and foreboding.

Books by Alexander Edwards

A Star Is Born
The Last of Sheila
McQ
Our Time
Katherine
The Black Bird

Published by
WARNER BOOKS

A STAR IS BORN

A STAR IS BORN

A New Novel by
Alexander Edwards
From The Screenplay by
John Gregory Dunne & Joan Didion
and Frank Pierson
Based On A Story by
William Wellman and Robert Carson

A Warner Communications Company

WARNER BOOKS EDITION

"WATCH CLOSELY NOW"
Words and Music by Paul Williams and Kenny Ascher

"SPANISH LIES"
Words and Music by Paul Williams and Kenny Ascher

"HELLACIOUS ACRES"
Words and Music by Paul Williams and Kenny Ascher

"EVERGREEN"
Words by Paul Williams
Music by Barbra Streisand

"THE WOMAN IN THE MOON"
Words and Music by Paul Williams and Kenny Ascher

"I BELIEVE IN LOVE"
Words by Alan and Marilyn Bergman
Music by Kenny Loggins

"WITH ONE MORE LOOK AT YOU"
Words and Music by Paul Williams and Kenny Ascher

ISBN 0-446-84214-1

Cover design by Sidney Ganis

Photograph section designed by Arthur Ritter

Warner Books, Inc., 75 Rockefeller Plaza, New York, N.Y. 10019

A Warner Communications Company

Printed in the United States of America

Not associated with Warner Press, Inc. of Anderson, Indiana

0 9 8 7 6 5 4

For Spike, who had a taste of Honey
and
For Honey, who had a taste of Spike

A STAR IS BORN

Chapter I

"John NORman! John NORman! John NORman!!" The chant was growing hideously loud, hideously insistent, rising in a swell above the steady, angry pounding of feet. "John NORman! John NORman!" The stomping shook the mammoth amphitheater, making the seats and the floorboards vibrate crazily. "John NORman!"

Nervously, Bobby Ritchie shook his long hair out of his eyes. Jesus, an impatient audience was like a goddamn Frankenstein monster! With fifty thousand enraged, yelling voices and a hundred thousand stamping feet. Although he was a seasoned pro, Ritchie was always antsy before a concert; now he was beginning to get what he would describe as "seriously nervous." He stood at the edge of the vast stage, wearing jeans and a Speedway T-shirt. One hand clutched a walkie-talkie, while the other hand anxiously clenched and unclenched, making his fingers ache. His eyes moved quickly from the restless crowd to his watch and back again. One hour and forty minutes past the official starting time, and still no John Norman Howard. Where the hell *was* he?

Rock music fans were accustomed to late starts; it had become so much an accepted part of the concert scene that, if a group were to start on time, any sold-out hall would likely be only half filled. As the longtime chief roadie for the Speedway, Ritchie knew this well, but he also knew that if you waited too long, the crowd could get out of hand and turn ugly. So ugly that even a great performance couldn't mollify them. And, thought Ritchie, his lower lip twisting, John Norman Howard had hardly been delivering "great" performances on this, the longest and most expensive tour in the group's long history.

Behind Ritchie on the stage loomed the source of most of the expense—tier upon tier of giant speakers, topped and banked by row after row of complex and sophisticated lighting equipment. A bewildering roster of amplifiers, consoles, control boards, and microphones littered the stage. The entire mass of technology was carefully interconnected by literally miles of color-coded wire and cable. A half-dozen roadies, like Ritchie sporting JOHN NORMAN HOWARD SPEEDWAY T-shirts, were still scrambling up, around, and under this superstructure, checking and testing connections and cues one more time. Bobby Ritchie and his crew had, as usual, begun to set up at noon, and though there remained little to be done after the band's afternoon sound check—which John Norman had also skipped—Ritchie always insisted that his boys look busy in front of the paying customers until the band hit the stage. The sound and light system was, after all, part of the attraction of a Speedway concert.

But the audience was tired of watching electricians. They were also tired of winging frisbees across the gigantic hall, of bouncing balloons from row to row, of yelling at their friends, of scrambling down from the balconies into the better seats and being ejected by security, of passing down the lightest of the chickies like a volleyball from hand to hand. Although the stadium smelled sweetly of marijuana, the audience was coming down off its high and getting anxious, saving its grass for the concert itself. In the first hour, the kids had set off their firecrackers and their cherry bombs and gotten into several hassles with the security people.

Security was always very heavy at a Speedway concert. The beefy young private guards, unarmed and recognizable only by their T-shirts emblazoned with the local promoter's logo, were everywhere inside the hall. They were backed up by dozens of local policemen, their faces stern and disapproving; the local cops hated the kids like poison. Arms crossed, bellies protruding over waists hung with official gear, the cops stood well back from the crowd whenever they could, talking among themselves, occasionally responding to loud, unintelligible squawks from their walkie-talkies with mumbles of their own. They knew that they could bust everybody here for something, but they also knew that they might have a riot on their hands, or at the least a lot of heat from the politicians beholden to the parents of these freaky kids. Yet, every now and then, one of them would dart forward as though he had eyes in the back of his head and tackle some skinny kid in jeans and haul him off to an exit.

"John NORman!! JOHN NORMAN!!!" The kids were yelling themselves hoarse, and the rhythmic, deafening pounding of their feet signaled the end of their patience. It was an always frightening sound, like an army of storm troopers on the march. Ritchie looked at his watch again. Jesus, where is that asshole? he thought. Raising his intercom to his lips, he spoke briefly into it.

At the other side of the apron, four road men stood poised over the electronic mixing board and light console. Like astronauts, they threw switches and turned dials. Instantly, the house lights dropped, taped music roared out of the speakers, and the elaborate, polychrome light show began. Momentarily stunned, the crowd recovered quickly and responded with a primal, gleeful howl. Ritchie smiled to himself in the dark, taking pleasure as usual in his power. It was like feeding animals, he thought. But he knew that this was only an appetizer and wouldn't hold them long. Soon they'd be demanding the real meal, the feast of music they had come for. Ritchie made his way backstage swiftly, with the night vision of a cat.

Backstage—actually *underneath* the stage—Ritchie found the usual pre-concert mob scene: a narrow, sloping, high-ceilinged, concreted space, airless and bathed in glaring fluorescent lights. The walls were plastered over with graffiti—"We love you, Stones"; "I love you, Humble Pie—Debbie in the third balcony"; "Call Linda for good head."

As always, the place was crammed with photographers, reporters for the music press, film crews, groupies, roadies, chauffeurs, truck drivers, cops, sheriff's deputies, janitors, and weird hangers-on. All of them had backstage passes pasted somewhere on their bodies, and all were shoving, sweating, drinking, smoking, and talking at once.

Ritchie made his way through the mob to the big, garage-like outer door, where he found the local promoter, his lanky frame propped against the wall. The promoter, seeing Ritchie, took a long, deliberate, significant stare at his watch. The two men then exchanged hard looks, but did not speak. Both could hear the dull thumping overhead as the foot-pounding began anew. There was nothing to say.

After a minute or two, the sound of motors made them raise their heads expectantly. Three large black limousines, John Norman's Cadillac in the lead, rounded the corner a block away and headed for the backstage door. With a squealing of tires, the Caddie pulled to a stop in front of them. Praise the Lord, thought Ritchie bitterly as he stepped forward quickly and yanked open the back door.

John Norman Howard, thirty-eight-year-old rock

star, stepped out of the limo gingerly. Haggard, more than a little drunk, and not knowing for certain quite where he was, he stood wobbling on the heels of his cowboy boots. A girl started to get out behind him, but Ritchie ignored her, grabbed John Norman's arm and began racing him through the door and up the corridor, running interference. Blocking a photographer from taking a shot, Bobby shouted at a small knot of people in their path. "Move it! Move it! The fucking star is comin' through!" As John Norman followed him automatically, like a zombie, the two men moved forward at a half-run, Ritchie barking orders into his intercom.

In one of the dressing rooms the rest of the band —Lee Dallas on bass guitar, Nicky Fiedler on drums, Pete Casselli on keyboard—had been whiling away the time passing joints, downing beers, and playing a game invented by Lee called "Kung Shoe." This personal form of martial art consisted of Lee standing at the far side of the room and kicking one of his heavy wooden clogs as hard as he could in the direction of the door. The object of the game was to have the clog fly through the air and hit the doorknob, while the rest of the guys bet on Lee or against him. In the many, many hours that the band had spent waiting for John Norman at concert after concert, Lee had grown quite proficient at Kung Shoe and there were rarely any winners who bet against him.

An intercom squawked in a roadie's hand as Ritchie's voice yapped into the dressing room. "Okay, gang, he's here!" Grabbing his clog, Lee shot out of the door, followed closely by Nicky and Pete. The band sprinted down the corridor in the direction of the stage.

John Norman met the Speedway at the foot of the short stairway leading to the stage. Ritchie was still holding tightly to his star's arm, as though afraid that John Norman would disappear again if he let him go. A roadie stripped off John Norman's Levi jacket and helped him into a white silk shirt. Another handed him a bottle of vodka, and John Norman took a long, grateful pull. Girls spoke eagerly to him, and he nodded back, but he didn't hear a word they were saying.

As yet another road man strapped the big Gibson Firebird over John Norman's shoulder, Lee Dallas sucked one last deep toke from a joint and stuck it in a groupie's mouth. Ritchie spoke rapidly now into his intercom, and the house lights went down again, leaving the center stage lit by a single white spot. The Speedway raced up onto the stage, but Ritchie held John Norman's elbow, keeping him back.

"Are you all right?" he shouted directly into John Norman's ear, but it came out a whisper over the din.

"Shit, yes!"

Holding out a small gold spoon filled with white powder, Ritchie let John Norman blow twice, once with each nostril. John Norman felt the cocaine traveling through his skull, clearing it and letting in a wave of crisp energy. Then, his feet upon the first stage step, John Norman threw back his head and took a long, deep swallow from the vodka bottle, handing it back to Ritchie. He stood for a moment, shaking himself like a dog, psyching himself up for the hours ahead, long grueling hours of playing and singing and showing off for an audience. Then he straightened.

Abruptly, Ritchie yelled "Now!" into his intercom and gave John Norman a shove up the steps. At once, the announcer's voice boomed and echoed throughout the arena.

"Ladies and gentlemen, the John Norman Howard Speedway!"

The stage lights came up and the crowd went

wild. Roadies scrambled over the stage, helping the band plug in their instruments and adjusting the small monitor speakers which faced the musicians. These were all-important; without them, the band would have no idea of how they themselves sounded. As they tuned up, John Norman and Lee Dallas strode back and forth, heads down, picking chords. A short drum roll from Nicky was followed by three or four keyboard riffs from Pete.

The men looked at each other, picking up each other's vibrations, smiling now. They were reacting with pleasure to the crowd's energy, expressed as one enormous scream. Dozens of hysterical girls rushed the solid wall of police lining the front of the stage.

John Norman, even more than the others, appeared transformed by the adulation. The lines of exhaustion faded from his face. His tall, slender body trembled with an excitement that was a mixture of the high moment and the cocaine. Under the lights that haloed his head and made him appear almost godlike, his deep-set blue eyes darted alertly from the crowd to the band. His face was framed by a graying brown beard and mustache, and fine brown hair fell in soft curls down the back of his neck and across his forehead. Ready now, he moved like a giant cat across center stage front, looking and feeling every inch the star. Grinning broadly, he hit a slow, loud lick on the Gibson.

Recognizing the chords, the crowd began to scream approval. The Speedway was off, into a hot number; it was their theme song, "Watch Closely Now," John Norman's best and most famous composition.

Watch closely now
Are you watching me now?
Your eyes are like fingers

They're touching my body
And arousing my soul
Riding the passion arising inside me
How high can I go?
You're comin' with me girl, I'm gonna show you how
When it's scary, don't look down

Watch closely now
Are you watching me now?
I see the hunger arise in your eyes
And it's urging me on
Higher and harder and faster and farther
Than I've ever gone
You're coming closer lady; don'tcha leave me now
We're gonna make it, don't look down

Baby I'm takin' me too many chances
With no net at all
Baby I'll teach you at least that you've
Got to be free when you fall

Watch closely now
Baby I'm takin' me too many chances
With no net at all
Baby I'll teach you at least that you've
Got to be free when you fall

Watch closely now
Are you watching me now?
I'm the master magician
Who's setting you free
From the lies you've been told
When they're breaking your back
Bring your last straw to me
I turn straw into gold
I'm gonna need you later, when you're not around
But I can take it, don't look down

Watch closely now. . . .
Are you watching me now?

As the set got underway, and the Speedway were rocking and rolling, Ritchie spent his time spot-checking his men. He had one ironclad rule for every roadie under him. No drugging or drinking until the performance was ended and the gear safely stowed away. How messed up they got afterward didn't interest him, but on *his* time they had to stay straight. Even the mildest violation of the rule resulted in summary dismissal, no matter how long you had been with the band or how clean your record. One stoned screw-up could blow an entire concert. Ritchie had been forced to fire only two of his crew in all his years with the Speedway. He chose his men carefully, and he paid them well. Each received between two and three hundred a week plus expenses. Other big-name acts paid twice that much and more on the road. But Ritchie, again as John Norman had taught him, paid his guys year round, on the road and off. There was always enough repair and studio work at home to justify it. In his career as chief roadie, he'd lost only two to other groups, and both of them had left to become chief roadies, a subtle compliment to Ritchie and John Norman.

Later, Bobby wandered back to the promoter's office to add up the night's take. Not only is the head roadie production manager and engineer, responsible for maintenance, movement, and performance of lights and sound equipment, he also handles all hotel accommodations for band and crew and serves as banker. On the road everybody, including John Norman himself, had to get his pocket money from Bobby Ritchie, keeper of the cash and the credit cards.

The promoter's office was a crowded little room, the walls plastered with posters for other rock concerts, prizefights, basketball games, a Billy Graham crusade. Eagerly assembled were the promoter, decked out in his self-consciously "hip" gear of patched jeans and tie-dye; the promoter's secretary, who was holding the strongbox that contained the night's receipts; the stadium owner, middle-aged and gone to fat; *his* secretary; and two Speedway roadies. Also present and watching very carefully was Gary Danziger, the Speedway's impish public relations man. He was dressed in one of his many natty velvet suits, this one dark and set off by a white shirt and striped silk tie. On his arm hung the latest in an endless parade of groupies, yet another bone-thin nymphet no more than half his age. A security officer, his head bandaged, stood in a corner of the room, stuffing his face morosely with french fries. As Ritchie entered, both secretaries were busy tabulating money on their adding machines, while the two roadies were counting ticket stubs, using calculators with lightning efficiency.

"That's $27,512," announced one of the roadies.

"That check?" asked Bobby, eyeing the secretaries. They both nodded.

"Count it out," ordered Ritchie.

As the heavy bundles of cash were handed to him in quick succession, he swept them into his attaché case, which was fastened to his wrist by a silver chain and delicate silver handcuff. The stadium owner who, like most of his breed, neither liked nor understood the music that was making him wealthy, watched the concert on a closed-circuit TV monitor as Ritchie counted.

"Jesus Christ, look at that!" he exclaimed in disgust. "I swear I can't see the attraction."

"You guys must be using the new math or something," Bobby Ritchie grumbled, continuing to count the take. It wasn't as large as usual, or as large as he'd expected.

"We gave away and comped half the house," the promoter protested hotly.

"Where was the promotion campaign? I didn't see any ads," Danziger shot back with equal heat.

"I see that kid in the street, I'm gonna leave him hanging from his jockstrap!" The injured cop, rubbing his wounded head, made his remark to no one in particular.

"You see this group we got booked next week? The Third Grade Band?" The fat stadium owner leered at Danziger's groupie.

"They're right outta the swamp!" she squealed.

"To promote what?" demanded the promoter. "Giveaways?" He was mad, too, because the John Norman Howard Speedway used to be a top draw—tickets sold out to the last stub two hours after the box office opened. Top draw and top money. Plenty for everybody, until that bastard Howard had started screwing up. Now the band was starting to slip, and the audiences were catching on. There were empty seats at every performance, and soon nobody would show up at all. Not John Norman, not the audience.

"So book the Ice Follies," Ritchie snapped, finishing his count. He fastened the attaché case shut and turned the combination lock, securing the money. Turning to leave, he stopped in the doorway and thumbed his nose contemptuously at the assembly. It was a gesture he'd picked up from John Norman, and it was coming in handy more and more often.

"Nice clean kids, them skaters," said the stadium owner with a wistful note in his voice. "On time, no dope, no fights, no aggravation." He wouldn't mind booking the Ice Follies, at that.

Back on stage, the long, hard-driving set was drawing to a close, the band winding down. Nicky, like most drummers, had stripped to the waist by now; Lee and Pete were down to sweat-soaked T-shirts. John Norman, his collarless pale silk shirt untucked and open to the waist, was dripping with sweat. His chest gleamed like the silver conchos on his broad leather belt. His curly hair was soaking wet and his beard glistened. Roadies were darting and crawling everywhere, replacing damp towels with fresh ones, refilling the big paper cups with heavy shots of vodka and orange juice, checking the sound system. As the number ended, John Norman unplugged his instrument and wandered to the side of the stage looking for a drink. Grabbing up a cup, he gulped it down with an intensity akin to savagery, the pale orange liquid running down both sides of his face.

Ritchie, standing in the wings, looked at John Norman and didn't like what he was seeing. The eyes were wild, the forehead deeply creased, the jaw slack. John Norman's neck was a bundle of corded, straining muscles. Christ, thought Ritchie, he looks like he spent the last two months in a concentration camp instead of on tour. Something was beginning to get to him. No, *everything* was beginning to get to him—the late nights, the booze, the chicks, the pills, the dope of all kinds. John Norman was looking more and more like a basket case.

The band was striking up another of their numbers, "Spanish Lies," but John Norman remained to the side of the stage in the dark, his head jutting slightly forward over slumped shoulders. Exchanging worried looks, the Speedway vamped it for a few moments until John Norman wandered back into the lights and plugged his guitar into its amp. As he moved up to the standing mike, they hit the opening chords for real.

John Norman opened his mouth to sing, lifted his right hand to his guitar to play, stamped the beat . . . and froze. Swiftly, he turned his back to his audience to cover himself. The band vamped again, but the crowd, which had already begun clapping the tempo of a number they knew so well, stopped in confusion. Cocking his head first to one side, then the other, John Norman hummed and scatted without conviction. Moving closer to Norman, but keeping his voice away from the microphone, Lee Dallas softly sang the opening bars, hoping to spark his leader's memory.

Don't be frightened baby come on in
Be somebody that you never been
Whatcha gonna do with all that sweet lovin' you
save
Ought to keep it rockin' from the cradle to the
grave . . .

Lee hit the melody playfully, as though John Norman were playing some kind of game. But he knew better.

"That's it? That's all there is?" John Norman's voice was blurry and high-pitched, like a whiny, dissatisfied child's. "That ain't much."

By now the audience was definitely restless, aware that something was going on. A few boos and hisses broke out here and there, mostly in the cheaper seats. Then more boos and catcalls, as every part of the stadium began to react. John Norman got through the first bar, but it was off tempo and half-hearted. Shaking his curly head in disgust, he unplugged his amplifier and headed for another drink. As the shouting grew louder and louder behind him, he turned to the audience and made them a mock-solemn bow.

"I'm sorry. I remembered the whole song two thousand three hundred and seventy-six times all the way through. That's two months and ten days singing the same damn ditty without a stop to piss."

There was a time when they would have found that very funny. Oh, yes, there had been a time when John Norman Howard could have done no wrong in their eyes; when his forgetting a lyric would have brought him cheers of encouragement, not boos and catcalls; when his making a wry joke would have brought the whole house to its feet. But that time was passing, had passed. Now they didn't find it funny. They stamped and yelled, a monster with hundreds and thousands of tongues and eyes and feet and one hostile, pulsating heart and mind, one set of negative vibrations.

Shrugging, John Norman moved back center stage and plugged in the Gibson. "If you don't like it, you can go to hell!" he told the monster, fury choking his voice.

Now the monster really went wild, turning into a hideous, snarling enemy. They began to chant, "Fuck YOU! Fuck YOU! FUCK YOU!!" as they clapped time to their own insidious music with their angry palms. John Norman strode to the back of the stage and picked up a handful of grotesque Halloween masks. He selected one for himself and handed the others to the band.

"What's this shit?" asked Lee.

"A little treat for the pigs," said John Norman. "Put it on. Let's play that little tune I gave you the other day." He grinned evilly and pulled his monster mask over his head. At once he and the Speedway were transformed into demons, frightening creatures twice normal size. Some of the chanting died away uncertainly, and the rest was overpowered by the heavily amplified rock music as the Speedway tore into "Hellacious Acres," a mean, contemptuous song that probably said more about what John Norman Howard thought of his fans—and himself—than anything he'd written before.

Look who's advertising
Billboards everywhere
"See Hellacious Acres
Your tailor made nightmare"
Traffic is backed up for miles
Attendants welcome you with devilish smiles

Steady. . . . steady. . . .
Have your tickets ready
Steady. . . . Steady. . . .

Go to hell
After dark
It's a sin filled city
An amusement park
It's a one way ticket to the other side
It's a Dr. Jekyll and a Mr. Hyde
See Lizzie Borden, she's one of the stars
And Tricky Dicky barkin'
Flashin' you his pardon
Jack the Ripper slashin' your tires

Even the devil needs money
Even the president needs money
To cover his overhead
That's why he opened Hellacious Acres
Or so his press agent said
Hang out with heavies
Your partners in crime
Forget the consequences, have a good time
Steady. . . . steady. . . .
Have your tickets ready
Steady. . . . steady. . . .

Go to hell
After dark
It's a sin filled city
An amusement park
And a one way ticket to the other side
It's a Dr. Jekyll   it's a Mr. Hyde
Get down and study suspicion and doubt
At Hellacious Acres
Listen mischief makers
Admission's free you pay to get out

Halfway through the song, John Norman pulled the mask from his overheated face and held it aloft, like an enemy's scalp. Strutting and stomping around the stage, he hurled the words into the audience's teeth, defying them, insulting them. And they reacted.

Frisbees began to fly toward the stage, followed by soda cans and lighted matches. Pennies rained down on the Speedway from the upper tiers, and gobs of popcorn, sticky with sugar syrup and peanuts. Cursing and jeering, the mob began to surge forward, all their anger directed at the stage. There were cries of "Rip-off!" and a few crazies began to storm the stage. A tight, angry grin on his face, John Norman tore off his guitar strap, brandished his instrument like a weapon at the audience, and flung it into their midst. Then he stripped off his shirt and threw it at them, strutting bare-chested around the stage with his fingers pushing his nose up in a repulsive pig-mask, an insult to the crowd.

Ritchie rushed onto the stage and grabbed at John Norman, who attempted to fight him off. But Ritchie was cold sober and his wiry body was very strong. Grabbing John Norman's arm in fingers of iron, he half pushed, half pulled him off the stage, shielding him from the crowd's view.

From the speakers around the auditorium, the announcer's voice boomed pleadingly, saying over and over again, "Ladies and gentlemen, please . . . please. . . ."

Another John Norman Howard concert had come to an unexpected end.

"Okay, girls, let's get the show on the road." Danziger bustled around importantly, sorting out girls like a butcher choosing cuts of meat. They grouped around him, smiling, anxious. This was the moment the groupies had been waiting for all evening. This was when they would get their chance at the musicians.

The limos were lined up waiting, surrounded by

the police and by stadium security personnel. With a practiced eye, Danziger picked out a handful of girls, pointing to each as he spoke.

"You . . . you're with Pete, and you, you go with Nicky. You. . . ." They fanned out to the big black cars, melting into the deep upholstery with little satisfied sighs and giggles.

"In the first car, honey . . . that's right," Danziger directed. "You . . . you get in this one. We'll sort out who's with who later."

A movement caught Danziger's eye. A girl, chunky and not as pretty as the rest, was heading for the third car.

"Hey, wait a minute," yelled Danziger. "Sorry, honey! We're overbooked tonight. Nobody in the cars we don't know."

John Norman, Ritchie, and the band came tearing down the corridor like escaping criminals, Ritchie clutching the attaché case as though it were loot from a bank job. Fans were already storming the alley and clawing their hysterical way past security as the musicians tumbled into the cars. Ritchie hustled John Norman and Pete into the third limo and followed them in, slamming the door just as the "fans" descended on them. The kids were shouting, slapping at the windows; the Caddie rocked slightly on its axles.

"Move it out! Move it out!" Ritchie shouted at the driver. This part always scares the shit out of me, he thought. You never know whether they're gonna kiss you or kill you. Probably both.

Big fat Mo, sitting at the wheel, threw the Caddie into gear, and the car gave a great leap forward. Expertly maneuvering it down the alley and out into traffic with one hand, Mo was polishing off a can of Spanish peanuts with the other. Nothing ever fazed him. Mo—sweet, dumb, gross and greasy Mo—was John Norman's driver, bodyguard, gopher, and friend. He almost never left his boss's side.

Slumped in the back seat, John Norman sat in silence. He barely listened as the others chattered among themselves, making small talk as though nothing had gone wrong, as though the concert had been a big success.

"I'm hungry," Pete was complaining.

"We could get some soft-shell crab," offered Dallas. "There's this place in San Diego, they fly it in."

"No," said Ritchie. San Diego was a long drive from Los Angeles, even for soft-shells. "We'll send Tony and David up to the stadium tomorrow with two Avis wagons," he told Mo.

"How many pieces of luggage?" Mo wanted to know.

"The same. Ninety-two, and some of the guys will have to double up. I need room for guys from the trucks."

"You get the Gibson back?" Pete asked Dallas, glancing out of the corner of his eye at John Norman.

"Yeah, the neck's all screwed up."

"How can they fuck up a fretless neck?" demanded Pete. "I never saw a fretless neck on a Gibson, anyway."

"You keeping the trucks over?" Mo asked Ritchie.

"I got to. We hafta allow for a rain date," explained the chief roadie.

"I worked a fairgrounds once in the rain," laughed Lee. "Every time I touched the mikes I got fucking electrocuted. It near cured me!"

"I'm hungry." John Norman broke his silence suddenly, unexpectedly. His voice was very flat, almost indifferent. The others shut up; the smoothly riding limo became an oasis of uncomfortable silence. Ritchie reached into his pocket and pulled out a small red capsule, handing it to John Norman. The rock star washed it down with a swallow from the bottle of vodka he held tightly clutched in his large hands. They drove on in silence.

"It was shit tonight," John Norman said finally.

"Get some sleep, or it will be shit again tomorrow," said Ritchie with quiet finality.

"You sound like my mother."

"I *am* your mother." And Bobby smiled bitterly.

Again, no one spoke as the Caddie moved rapidly along the freeway toward the inevitable Holiday Inn.

"I know an intern who can get adrenalin. Pure adrenalin." The squeaky little voice popped up from the corner of the back seat. "He steals it from the emergency hospital."

Stunned, they all turned in the direction of the voice to discover a skinny little groupie curled up in the corner of the big dark car. In the rush and confusion, nobody had noticed her. Now they stared at her blankly.

"You shoot it in the arm," she continued with a grin, enjoying the attention of the rock musicians. "It makes a big ball, and then you squeeze it down flat. It only makes you feel scared for about a minute. And then . . . wheeee!" She flapped her arms, pantomiming a flight to the moon.

"She yours?" Ritchie addressed Lee. Dallas shook his head.

"She's yours?" the road manager demanded of Pete.

"Uh-uh." Another negative.

"Ask Mo if she's his." She wasn't.

As they pulled into the lot of the Holiday Inn, the familiar sign flashing overhead, the other two limos were just arriving. Doors were pushed open and the band and crew members—tired, subdued—tumbled out, followed closely by the groupies, who tagged along behind them like obedient puppies. Only John Norman remained behind, still slumped in the back seat of his car. Ritchie waited by the Caddie door, his hand on the handle, expectant.

"I can do you, too." The weird little stowaway

groupie invited John Norman, looking at him longingly.

"I got all the adrenalin I need," John Norman replied, slamming the door.

"Sweetheart, excuse me." Bobby Ritchie moved the girl aside roughly. He leaned down to the open window. "Let's go," he ordered John Norman.

John Norman leaned his head back against the upholstery and closed his eyes. He looked, suddenly, five years older.

"You gotta get some sleep," said Ritchie firmly. He'd been through this shit before.

"I can't sleep," John Norman said softly. Then he opened his eyes and smiled at the road manager. "Hey, Bobby, drop the whistle and the clipboard and come out and smile, or get drunk or anything, you heartless bastard."

But Ritchie just stared. John Norman leaned forward and tapped the driver's shoulder. "Floor it, Mo," he ordered.

"Where you goin'?" demanded Bobby Ritchie. "You gotta go to bed. We got a gig tomorrow you can't afford to fuck up, slick. We busted our ass to get it together. We had to book four other acts to make sure we got the people there. Plus a personal guarantee from me and Brian and the guys that you'd show and be straight enough to remember the damn words. His ass is on the line, my ass, everybody's ass. Fifty thousand people. They're waitin' to see if you still got anything to show."

He stopped for breath and to see if there would be any response from John Norman. There wasn't; he might as well have been shouting at a stone wall.

"God damn it!" yelled Ritchie, really angry now. "We had to get a court order to get the cops to let you on at all, after the Detroit number. The guys are pissed, and they're right. Sittin' around two, three hours to go on with a cold crowd and you stoned out of your fuckin' skull."

"Floor it," John Norman told Mo.

"You blow this one, motherfucker, you blow the whole thing!" Ritchie screamed. "The tour is over! For *everybody*! You dig?"

Mo slowly pulled away, wheeling the car out of the lot toward the freeway. They drove awhile in silence, Mo with his eyes on the road, John Norman sprawled alone in the back seat, his head thrown back, his blue eyes shut.

"Where to?" asked Mo at last.

"Back ten years," said John Norman quietly.

Chapter II

He was tired, taut with tension and the lack of sleep, filled with too much coke and booze and too many reds, tingling with a residual energy from the concert and a heavy, leaden feeling of disappointment and shame. He'd been feeling a lot of that lately. But mostly, he thought, it was the lack of sleep. Hell, sometimes he thought he'd never sleep again. He had to go somewhere, be with people who didn't know him, didn't claw at him, didn't expect so much from him. He was tired, bone-deep tired, and most of all, he was tired of being John Norman Howard.

"Pull in here," he told Mo. "Here" was a club, and John Norman could hear music coming from inside. Suddenly, warmth and music was exactly what he wanted. And a drink.

He knew this place as soon as he walked in the door and nearly fell down the steps. He'd been here a million times before. Only it was in Phoenix, not Los Angeles. In Phoenix, in Tucson, in San Antonio, in Denver . . . what the hell was the difference? These places were all the same. A lot of red brick, stained glass, and no booze. There would be a dart game and some amateur entertainment, some would-be Joni Mitchell or John Denver or Kris Kristofferson. It was a hangout for schoolteachers and accountants, for hardhats and copy boys and those junior "executives" who wore long hair and smoked grass and thought they were hip. Well, what the hell, maybe he wouldn't get in trouble here, for a change. As for booze . . . he peered into the paper bag clutched tightly in his hand. The vodka bottle was nearly full. That would hold him for a couple of hours; when it was empty, he'd split for somewhere else.

It was dark in the club, and John Norman kept bumping into tables and chairs as he made his way down front. He wanted a good table, wanted to hear some music. Three chicks were standing on the tiny stage, singing their little hearts out, and John Norman felt like giving them a little professional encouragement. They weren't bad. He was hungry; he'd get him some chicken and some french fries and he'd listen to the music and clap and drink his vodka and it would all be mellow.

But first he'd hafta stop bumping into everything. And who were these people pulling at him, and calling out to him? Shit, they recognized him. He might have known it.

"It's John Norman Howard!"

"Can I have your autograph for my daughter?"

"He looks shorter in person, doesn't he?"

"A friend of a friend of mine's neighbor had him once. Know what I mean?"

John Norman stood for a moment, confused by all the attention, until a hostess came to his rescue. Taking him by the hand, she pulled him down front and over to the side of the stage where the girls were still singing. There were three of them, two black girls who made a frame for the white girl in the center, a little girl with a large voice. The white girl's hair was a mass of bubbling golden curls under the overhead lights, and her slim body was dressed in a pair of tight jeans rolled up over knee-high boots, a man's collarless shirt, and sequinned suspenders. Cute, John Norman registered automatically as he found his seat. The hostess hovered over him, an order pad in her hand.

"My name is John Norman Howard," he said unnecessarily. He couldn't think of anything else to say.

"Wine, beer, or herbal tea?" asked the hostess.

It was the same in Phoenix, Tucson, San Antonio, and Denver. "Those are the options?"

"Right." The hostess didn't bat an eye. She'd been around, this one, and she'd seen John Norman Howard before. Plenty of them. Up on the stage, the girls were singing about a queen bee who ruled her hive and outlived her mates, but the noise level in the club had risen sharply with John Norman's entrance, and it was hard to hear the singing. Everybody was watching the rock star.

John Norman put his paper bag on the table. Smiling prettily at the bored hostess, he said, "How about you bring me the herbal tea? Iced herbal tea. But put the ice in one glass and the herbal tea in another."

The hostess glanced at him suspiciously, then at the obviously bottle-shaped paper bag, from which John Norman was now pulling a large bottle of vodka. The girls had stopped singing, aware that nobody was listening, and the white girl was climbing down off the stage, her microphone in her hand.

"We don't have a license, so what are you planning to do with that bottle?" A worried look appeared on the hostess's face; this could be trouble for everybody.

"I'm planning to open it, first," said John Norman, suiting the action to the words.

Sitting down beside him, the hostess leaned forward cajolingly. "Why don't you just give me that bottle," she cooed, reaching for it.

John Norman snatched the bag away, out of her

reach. "WHAT ARE YOU GOING TO DO WITH MY BOTTLE?" he asked, then stopped abruptly, as he heard his own voice booming out of the club's public address system. He turned his chair half around. A slim, white arm extended before him, the hand holding a microphone to his lips. John Norman followed the line of the arm upward. It was the blond singer.

"You're blowing my act," she said, looking him in the eye. She said it simply, directly, without malice. It was a statement of fact.

But it hurt. John Norman realized suddenly that he had made a fool of himself again and that this girl was putting him down for it, putting him down and he deserved it. She took her work seriously; that much was evident, and he had no business—as a professional himself—ruining another professional's efforts. Feeling this suddenly very deeply, he looked up at her, mute.

"Okay?" The girl's full lips twisted in a little wry smile, and she raised one eloquent eyebrow.

"Okay!" John Norman raised his hands, palms outward, in apology. "Hey, I'm sorry. I swear! I got the manners of a hog!"

The piano player and drummer picked up the beat again, and the girl began singing as she backed away from the rock star's table and continued singing as she mounted the stage again. John Norman listened for a few bars. This girl was good, he thought with a sudden excitement, as the rest of the trio joined in. Really good. The song came to an end and John Norman clapped like a maniac, oblivious to the fact that he was the only one applauding; the others were too busy watching the big-name star who had appeared so suddenly in their midst. But as he kept clapping, they joined in, first in twos and threes, then in a burst of sustained applause.

The girl on the stage, glad to have her audience back, gave her backup a relieved smile, and began another number. John Norman leaned forward to give her his full attention and a flashbulb exploded suddenly in his face, catching him off guard and blinding him for a moment. A tourist had sneaked up behind him for a Polaroid picture, and John Norman, outraged, thumbed his nose at the upstart.

He was still blinking and trying both to see and to hear when a tall, beefy man, dragging his wife behind him, pushed his way over to the table.

"John Norman Howard! How're ya doin'?"

"Shinin', man." John Howard made the response without turning around. It was the barest of courtesies, designed to make anybody with any sense go away.

But it was evident that this beefy man was short on sense. "Hey, John Norman Howard! Sonuvabitch, you ain't goin' dry while I'm around." Taking a bottle from his hip pocket, he poured booze into a glass and pressed it on John Norman. The singer accepted it, but it wasn't because he wanted the drink or the man's attention. He was trying to listen to the singing, and what he wanted was some quiet and the chance to do just that. He took a sip, watching the girl up there on the stage.

He wondered if she knew just how good she really was. The voice was full and melodious, with an impressive range, but her phrasing and the feeling she put into a lyric were so pure and impressive that she could have got away with less voice. She was a natural; it was as simple as that. A real talent, one in a million.

As she sang, John Norman looked at her closely. She wasn't conventionally pretty, but she had a unique quality that was better than mere prettiness. Her hands, for example, long and slim with long, tapered oval nails—they were the most beautiful hands he'd ever seen in his life. Even duchesses didn't have fingers like those. And her hair. Thick, glossy, and tightly curled, it tumbled down over her forehead and neck in little ringlets so full of life that John Norman found himself wanting to touch them. Her body was good and her mouth was luscious, but it was her eyes that arrested John Norman and held him wordless. They were large and light-colored, deeply set like his own, but he couldn't tell from where he sat whether they were blue or green. And, suddenly, he found himself wanting to know. He *needed* to know, and he didn't understand where that need was coming from.

"I'm Marty. This here's Sheila, she's a fan of yours." It was the beefy man and his wife; they were still hanging around.

"Sheila, how you doin'?" John Norman responded automatically, trying to be polite while listening.

"Saw you on TV," the man persisted. "I thought you were lousy, but Sheila here liked you, didn't you, Sheila?"

"I thought he was okay," his wife replied with almost no interest and certainly no enthusiasm. Some fan!

"Let's listen to the act, man," said John Norman quietly.

Up on the stage, standing between Phyllis and Sydelle like the cream in an Oreo cookie, Esther Hoffman sang and kept her eyes fixed on John Norman Howard. She had recognized him as soon as he'd stumbled into the place and had put an extra little something into "Queen Bee," aiming it directly at him. Not that it had done her any good. He was too drunk to see where he was going, let alone to care about some coffeehouse singer. It wasn't personal, she told herself. It was one professional acknowledging another. Professional, hah! He was a stoned, strung-out rock star while she was still belting them out in a nowhere joint like this one. Still, he had paid her some attention after she'd zinged him with the mike; he'd applauded her, and he seemed to want to listen.

But he was trouble, Esther sensed. Trouble followed this man wherever he went, wherever he was recognized. She'd heard some of the stories, and she could see him now for herself. Drunk and stoned, and terribly vulnerable. What was he doing here, all by himself, among these people who knew his face and name and thought they knew the man himself? What was he looking for? Where were his friends, and why did they let him go out alone in this condition? Who was looking after him?

"Let's listen to the act, man," John Norman was saying to Marty.

The beefy man waved one hairy, negative paw. "That's shit. Why don't choo get on there, sing us a song?"

"Hey, lighten up," said John Norman mildly, turning around. "They're tryin' to sing. It's hard, man."

Immediately, the man bridled in outrage. "Don't tell me what's hard," he shouted. "You . . ." he turned to where the people at the next table were shushing him. "Shut up you goddamn selfs!" He was deeply angry now. No punk rock-and-roll faggot was going to tell *him* life was hard! When he labored as many hours a day as he did, in the broiling sun, in the freezing rain, to come home at night to this sour-faced bitch, Sheila, who didn't appreciate anything he tried to do for her. Well, by God, he was doing something for her now! She liked this faggot's music, she was going to hear it!

"She bought all your goddamn records," he shouted at John Norman. "Now get on up there and sing for Sheila, John Norman!"

A deep weariness washed over John Norman's soul. He'd been here before, so many, many times. What did these people ever want from him? Why didn't they ever let him alone? Why did his mere presence among them bring out so much rage and frustration? He wasn't asking much, just to be allowed to have a drink and listen to this girl's golden world of a voice. Why couldn't he ever, *ever* be allowed even that much? When had he made the bargain with the devil that took little things like this away in exchange for a fame that left a bitter taste in his mouth and a fortune he couldn't find a fuckin' dime of?

"Not tonight, Sheila," he sighed. Then he turned to the big man, who was glaring at him through tiny, pig-ugly eyes. "Look, mister," he said reasonably, still hoping to put off the inevitable, "it's late and I'm tired. Why don't you two go back to your own table and have yourselves somethin' good to eat?"

"What the hell is that supposed to mean?" Marty's huge hands curled themselves into giant, hairy fists.

Suddenly, John Norman laughed. Why postpone it? Why not just get it over with and get the hell out of here? He held his drink out, grinning. "Listen, this drink isn't worth listening to your mouth."

That did it. With a howl of rage, the big man leaped forward, straight into John Norman's waiting fist. It wasn't much of a fight as fights go; John Norman had been in many more serious. There was more pushing and shoving than actual hitting, but they managed to make a lot of noise, break a number of tables and chairs, and disrupt the club entirely. Most of the customers of the little club were pacifists, but a handful did join in, yelling happily and swinging wildly, and occasionally a punch would connect and deck somebody. It was a confused melee, a brawl, with John Norman and the big man at the center of it.

Up on the tiny stage, Esther and the girls were carrying on in the best show-must-go-on tradition, although nobody even knew they were there. *Oy*, thought Esther, I need this? Phyllis kept giving her nudges and tweaks that said plainly, let's get the hell out of here, but something kept Esther glued to the mike, even when she had to duck a punch. She was watching John Norman at the heart of the action. It seemed to her as though he'd get hurt if she took her eyes off him, as though he'd be safe as long as she watched. She knew it was dumb, but she couldn't shake that feeling. She saw him go down once, and her mouth grew dry and she lost the lyric until he stood up and went on swinging.

"Hell of a way to behave! The hell with it!" Runyon, the club owner, strode into the melee with a baseball bat in his hands, restoring order in the only way he knew how—by force. "All of you get outta my place! I'm closed!"

The fight began to break up as the customers headed for the exits. But John Norman and the large man were still filled with nervous energy, still determined to slug it out until one of them didn't get up. By now, a number of people were holding them apart while they yelled insults at each other and strained to break free. John Norman was up, exhilarated. He felt the cold, sluggish blood turning warm, then hot, and racing through his veins. He was tingling; maybe this was what he'd needed after all! The big man had some friends with him—hell! he'd take them *all* on!

"Let's get out of here. Through the back. . . ." A hand tugged at John Norman's arm. He turned around. The blond singer, her face anxious, was pulling at him, trying to lead him away. At once, his temperature dropped, and he lost interest in the fight. Allowing her to set the course, he followed the girl behind the little stage and into the back of the club.

"Son of a bitch!" John Norman hopped up and down, his face contorted in pain. It was dark in this frigging place, and there were exposed pipes and old furniture everywhere, lying in wait for his shins. It was like going through a field of land mines.

"Come *on*!" She could see in the dark, like a cat. Her eyes must be cat-green, he found himself thinking as he followed her through the maze of dark doorways and out of the rear exit. She held his hand tightly, dropping it only when they emerged from the club into the parking lot.

Cars were zooming out of the lot, as all the customers headed home at the same time. At a distance, John Norman and Esther could see the big man and his friends emerging from the front entrance, looking around them furiously. They were shouting and gesticulating, and were obviously still out to taste John Norman's blood as soon as they located it.

Shit! They'd located it! Now that they'd spotted John Norman, they were running at full speed across the parking lot. John Norman grabbed up the blond girl's hand and ran with her in the direction of his limousine. Behind them, coming out of the rear door, were Esther's singing partners, yelling and waving at them to stop.

"Just once," hissed John Norman through clenched teeth, "I'd like to go someplace without a hassle!"

"You're not responsible, right?" the singer asked on a note of sarcasm.

The men were getting closer, yelling for John Norman to stop and wait until they caught up and killed him. He picked up speed, almost dragging the girl behind him. Her curls bobbed on her neck as she ran.

"All I ever want is to slip in and out quietly," John Norman protested. "I don't even like to be recognized."

By now they had reached the Caddie; Mo had the doors open, ready. Without thinking, John Norman began to push Esther ahead of him into the back seat. Across the parking lot, the heavies were moving a little more slowly, since they had to keep dodging the cars pulling out. Phyllis and Sydelle came running up from the other direction.

"Right," agreed Esther, casing the limo with a raised eyebrow. "You really slip around town unnoticed in this thing." The yelling had reached her ears, and she suddenly realized what bedlam was approaching on all sides. Trying to back out of the car, she decided that all she wanted was to mind her own business and go home.

"Hey, wait a second," she protested. "You go on, quick."

But John Norman, standing behind her, stood firm. "I'm not going without you," he said, shaking his head.

"Go *on*!" yelled Esther, half in and half out of the car. "Oh, God, here they come!"

She looked around wildly. Marty and company were only about one car's length away, and mad as hell. Without a second thought, she piled into the back seat of the Caddie and John Norman followed her in the same second, slamming and locking the door. Mo was already behind the wheel, and the big car pulled smoothly out of its parking space and headed for the exit.

Suddenly, the car rocked with heavy pounding. Marty and his friends were running alongside the limo, slamming at the hood and the glass with their huge, angry fists. Esther held her breath until the car picked up speed and left the belligerents far behind them. She turned and looked through the tinted rear glass. She could see Phyllis and Sydelle waving "Come back," and the men shaking their fists. Then they turned out of the exit and onto the street and she couldn't see anything more. Sinking back onto the comfortable upholstery, she turned to face her fellow passenger.

Esther's feelings were mixed, and the confusion was making her nervous. Here she was, snug in a Cadillac with Mr. Rock and Roll, and he didn't even know her name! He probably didn't care much, either. Not only that, he'd busted up her act, and she wasn't happy about that. There was something so unprofessional about it that it made her mad. Not to mention that she didn't even like rock and roll much; it wasn't her kind of music. Her kind came from the heart, not the belly. Her kind involved some serious listening to the lyrics, the setting of a mood, the reaching out with her voice to touch her listeners and make them her friends. She wanted her audience to understand *feelings*, their own as well as hers. This guy got up on a giant stage, plugged in his guitar and made an electric assault on all your senses, battering them down. His audiences were always stoned and tripping, and even if they were in shape to listen to the words, you couldn't even understand them, anyway, because they all sounded like "oooohhh, baby" filtered through Cream of Wheat. So why was she so nervous? He was attractive; maybe that was why. Older than she, much older. His hair and beard were getting very gray and he wasn't her type at all, but he *was* attractive. There was something about him that kept her looking at him, and it made her nervous. She didn't like the way he was looking at her, either. Like a hungry cat at a particularly juicy mouse. She was used to fielding passes, God knows, but this man was trouble. With a capital John Norman Howard. If that didn't spell trouble, nothing did.

"What am I doing here? You're crazy!" Esther squeaked.

"And you're one hell of a singer," replied John Norman. He was peering at her, trying to see the color of her eyes, but the car was too dark; it would have to wait until later. He liked this girl, she was a stone gas. There was something different about her, something fresh and original, something funny and touching. She made him feel good. She was as different from the skinny, strung-out goofballs who followed bands around as the sun was from a flashlight. There was a warmth about her that attracted him. He had no real plans for her. He wanted to ball her, of course, and maybe to introduce her around to some people in the music business who could help her. She was good, and she could make it, maybe even to the top. He wanted this curly-haired girl to think well of him, to remember him with fondness as a good friend and a good lay. Why not? She'd be a lot better off than she was now. I mean, what did she have? A dumpy little trio in a little dump. That was show biz? She deserved better, and he'd see that she got it before he moved on.

"Yeah? How could you tell I'm one hell of a singer?" she demanded. "You were talking through my whole song!"

"That guy wouldn't shut up!" John Norman defended himself.

"So you had to hit him?"

"What was I supposed to do . . . let him pulp me?" protested John Norman.

"All you did was to make him a hero," Esther pointed out angrily. "Now he'll go around telling how he punched out some sissy faggot rock star. You gave him a story for the next couple of years. Are you drunk?" She was talking so fast that her words were blurring, tumbling out over themselves.

"Jesus, you talk a lot," marveled John Norman, grinning at her.

Esther blushed, and one of her long fingers twisted a curl of her hair. "I always talk a lot when I'm nervous," she explained. Then she turned away from him slightly. "At least I don't jabber while some poor kid is up there singing her heart out."

John Norman's grin grew wider. "Some kid," he scoffed. "You know, you really knocked me out in there," he told her.

"Yeah?" It was obvious that Esther didn't believe him. "You really knocked me out in there, too—you drove out my whole audience! What were you doing there, anyway?" She looked at him curiously; he was a being totally new to her.

"I can't sleep," said John Norman simply.

"Where we headin'?" asked Mo from the front seat, without turning his massive head.

"Back to the Holiday Inn," ordered John Norman.

Esther leaned forward. "211 Orchid," she said firmly, brooking no argument. "That's in Hollywood."

Mo waited a beat for John Norman to contradict her, but no word was forthcoming. John Norman had obviously accepted the blond's direction and interpreted it as an invitation, for Mo could see him relax in the back seat and smile. Mo shrugged and gave it the old college try.

"I'm supposed to get you back to the Holiday Inn," he told his boss.

John Norman's only reply was to put his finger on a button. Instantly, a wall of glass raised itself between the front seat and the back, cutting him off from Mo's comments and reminders.

"I slept in that motel thirty-eight straight nights," he told Esther with a rueful twist of his lips.

"You only played here one night," the girl pointed out.

John Norman nodded agreement. "Yeah, right, but it's the same motel. They just ship it ahead of us. Knock it down and pack it in big semis. Fifty-four semis. The Magic Fingers go in the lead van."

"What are Magic Fingers?" Esther asked with a curious smile.

John Norman laughed out loud in amazement. "I got to teach you everything!" he marveled. "It's a massage thing in the bed. You drop in a quarter and . . ."

"Aren't you embarrassed driving around in this thing?" the girl interrupted hastily. "Isn't this the kind of car they use for funerals?" She touched the upholstery with her long, slim fingers and pretended to be very interested in the car's interior.

"You change the subject a lot," commented John Norman.

"What was the subject?" asked Esther, her eyes innocent saucers.

"I'm trying to tell you how you sing," he said quietly. "Do you fish?"

"I sing like a fish?" Shut up, she told herself. Shut up. You're not funny. Don't try to be funny.

But John Norman paid no attention to her feeble little joke. "There's a rush, a little ball of fire inside that happens when you hook into a really big marlin," he said slowly, searching for the comparison that he could best express, best understand himself. "You never forget it. That's you. Singing."

It had the ring of truth; Esther couldn't doubt his sincerity. His words gave her a thrill of pleasure, which turned instantly to shyness. "That's nice," she said quietly. "Coming from you."

"So what the hell are you doing singing there?" demanded John Norman. "Waiting for Ahmet Ertegun to walk in?"

"You never had to scratch, right?" countered Esther hotly, her curls tossing.

"Yeah," replied John Norman with a tinge of bitter sarcasm. "I was born number eight with a bullet."

"We're doing our suffering," Esther explained simply. "I think they call it paying our dues. It's the first step, isn't it?" She wasn't ashamed of anything she'd accomplished so far; it had all been on her own.

"It's overrated. Help from a friend is better," John Norman told her.

Esther bristled. A handout! Was she being offered a handout? Was he trying to bullshit her? Her lower lip stuck out and her eyes narrowed as she glared at him. "What are you offering?" she challenged him. "A record contract? God, that's so cheap!" She turned away from him and moved closer to her side of the car, as though looking for an escape.

"What's wrong? What did I do to you?" demanded John Norman. "Did we meet somewhere in a former existence, or what?" He couldn't figure this girl out; anybody else would have jumped into his pants head first at the merest mention of help from "a friend" as important as he was. And this girl was giving him the freeze.

"You drove out my whole audience!" Esther hollered, exasperated. Couldn't this shitkicker get that through his stoned-out skull? Did he think she was some kind of amateur singing for nickels wrapped in newspaper? Was she supposed to kiss his helping hand after he'd broken up her entire act?

"I thought we just settled that. I'm sorry."

"Well, I don't forgive easily," sniffed Esther.

Suddenly, John Norman pulled the car door open. The car was doing fifty-five on the freeway, but the tall rock singer slid over toward the open door and poked one long leg out.

"I'll just get out here," he told her casually, as he began to move his other leg along the seat to the door.

With a shriek of horror, Esther leaned over and grabbed him, tugging him back inside the speeding automobile.

"What are you doing?" she yelled, terrified.

"I'll kill myself, it's the least I can do," John Norman said with a small wistful smile.

"Don't say that!" hollered Esther. What a crazy sonuvabitch! She wouldn't put any kind of *mishegoss* past this show-off nut! "Get back in here," she urged, tugging him away from the door and toward the middle of the back seat and safety.

"Never talk about it any more?" John Norman bargained with a cunning grin.

Speechless, Esther nodded her curls in a promise. With a satisfied smile, he pulled his leg inside the car and slammed and locked the Caddie door. Esther blew out her cheeks in a sigh of relief. As for Mo, he hadn't given more than one backward glance.

"My God, he didn't even slow down!" exclaimed Esther. What kind of people were these, who made jokes about death? Didn't they know that death was final and forever and nothing to laugh about? What was she getting herself into with this nut, with his deep, rolling laugh and his deep blue eyes? If she were smart, *she'd* get out, even at fifty-five miles an hour!

"Never talk about it again . . . never question . . . never look back. Think like a bullet . . ." John Norman delivered his philosophy.

The limousine pulled over to a curb, and John Norman looked up, startled. It was 211 Orchid; they were home. He peered out of the window and saw a set of 1930s stucco apartments with "Oleander Arms" in fancy script over the entrance. A few faded palm trees, dry from lack of rain, gave the place a rundown air that even the fragrant oleanders couldn't mask. It was a Hollywood bungalow complex like a thousand others; clean, cheap, and serviceable. Well, who was he to criticize? He lived in a Holiday Inn, didn't he?

He stepped out on the pavement and turned to give Esther his hand. She followed him out, smoothing her jeans and giving her shoulder bag a hitch. As she searched in her purse for the keys, Mo lowered the window on the curb side.

"You check into a motel and phone Bobby," John Norman instructed him. Then he turned to Esther, who stood holding out her hand for him to shake.

"Good night," she said pleasantly, turning to go inside.

"Hey, wait a minute!" This wasn't what John Norman had in mind. "Are you married?" he asked her, feeling a little foolish.

"Not now." Esther shook her head. "Why? Are you?" Then she put her hand to her mouth. "Esther, how ridiculous!" she chided herself. "You read about it in the entertainment section. I'm sorry. I'm not used to the rich and famous. It makes me act . . . stupid."

She was talking sixteen to the dozen again, and John Norman realized that she was nervous. It tickled him, being able to recognize things about her. He was getting to know this girl, and it made him feel good.

"You're acting okay," he assured her. "I haven't been acting so hot. Let's start clean," he offered. "You have a beautiful mouth . . ."

With her keys in her hand, Esther turned to face him.

"Even though I talk too much?" she asked.

"And a great ass," John Norman added. "You live alone?"

Esther nodded. "Uh-huh."

"Terrific!" This was the best news John Norman had heard all night. He took a step forward, but the girl held up one warning hand.

"I wouldn't send up fireworks about it," she told him dryly.

"Actually, I'd like to come in," said John Norman with his best boyish smile. He was enjoying this; he hadn't had to chase a woman in years, and it pleased him to think he hadn't forgotten how. This was some lady!

"Actually, no," said the lady.

"What's wrong with me? Don't you like me?"

"I don't get shipped in the van with the Magic Fingers," said Esther, regarding him thoughtfully. It was *her* philosophy, based on a sense of her own value. She turned to go, and a sudden pang took her totally by surprise. She was overwhelmed by a sense of sorrow so great that she had to draw a deep breath to fight it. This was ridiculous! Here was a million-dollar rock-and-roll star with a chauffeured limousine and his own private stock of booze and his Magic Fingers and *she* was feeling sorry for *him*! Why was she pitying him? Yet, she remembered how she had felt when she saw him from the stage. Vulnerable and alone—that's how she'd seen him. Vulnerable and alone. Lonely. Goddamn it, he probably had a hundred hangers-on and a thousand girls all lined up crying for it, why the hell did *she* have to perceive him as vulnerable and alone?

Esther turned back. John Norman was still standing there, watching her. "Listen, you want to come back for breakfast," she said slowly, "I'll make beaten biscuits."

"I don't eat breakfast," shrugged John Norman, his eyes searching her face.

Esther gave him a little, crooked smile. "Well, thanks, anyway, for the ride." She turned to go once more.

"All right!" snapped John Norman, surrendering. "Damn it! We'll have beaten biscuits together." He looked at his wristwatch; the numerals glowed redly in the dark. "It's four o'clock now. I'll be up at six."

"Make it seven," said Esther with a smile, closing the door.

Biting his lip, John Norman strode back to the Caddie.

"We goin' back?" Mo wanted to know.

"No!" John Norman was pissed off. "Goddamn it!"

"Bobby's going to have a shit fit," Mo pointed out equably. Bobby was always having a shit fit. It was part of the job.

John Norman wasn't listening. "Get me up at seven," he ordered, crawling into the back seat of the Caddie and curling up to sleep. As soon as his head touched the seat, he drifted off. It was the first sleep he'd had in days, and it was dreamless.

As he rang the bell of her bungalow apartment, John Norman knew he looked like five miles of unpaved road. His clothes were a rumpled mess, his hair was tangled, his eyes were sunken like a couple of piss-holes in the snow. He was monumentally hung over, and his head was splitting wide open. Christ, I need a drink, he thought as he pressed the bell again. What the fuck am I doing here at seven o'clock in the fucking morning, waiting to see a girl whose name I can't even remember? Did she tell me her name? Even if this girl were Candy Bergen, who in his right mind could get it up at seven in the morning?

The door opened a crack, and he heard the night chain rattle as it was removed. She was obviously having second thoughts, too, he guessed. Then Esther opened the door all the way and stood there, looking at him.

He'd been wrong. They weren't cat-green at all, but blue, deep blue, bluer even than his own, and fringed by smoky black lashes that set them off like sapphires. They were the bluest eyes he'd ever seen. Her hair was as soft as feathers, he thought, and his fingers suddenly ached to touch her curls. He raised his hand and remembered the box he was holding.

"Breakfast," said John Norman, handing it to her.

She ripped open a corner of the box and peered inside. "Sausage pizza? For breakfast?" she asked doubtfully.

"No, no." John Norman shook his head. "Pepperoni." He smiled at her. "You got the biscuits made?"

It was Esther's turn to smile now. She gave a little shrug. "I never made biscuits in my life," she confessed. "I was just doing a number on you."

"I knew that. That's why I brought the pizza." He

followed her into the apartment and headed straight for the phone. As he gave the operator his credit card number and placed the call to Phoenix, he looked around the apartment in surprised pleasure. It was nice. Really nice. Not tacky at all, but real pleasant. The floors were covered with floral print rugs, and the furniture was old but carefully chosen and in perfect condition. The more he looked around, the better he liked it. The little apartment was scrupulously neat and clean, and fresh flowers stood around cheerfully in vases. It was a home. Even the pictures on the wall pleased him, although he didn't recognize them as Icarts or Parrishes.

As the operator put through his call, John Norman yelled into the kitchen, where Esther had gone with the pizza box.

"You got a drink around here?"

"You mean like orange juice?" she called back.

"You going to try to improve my character?"

"It could use it."

On the other end of the phone, Bobby Ritchie's voice was raised in excitement.

"Hey, mother!" John Norman shouted into the phone. Then, to Esther, "Beer? Wine? Anything?" He held the phone away from his ear as Ritchie's voice broke the decibel record. "I'm okay, for Christ's sake. I'm in L.A." he told Bobby. "Who quit first?" he yelled in the direction of the kitchen.

Esther appeared in the kitchen doorway, looking puzzled. She was wearing a lace-trimmed satin dress or nightgown, John Norman couldn't tell which, but she looked beautiful in it and the gleaming texture aroused him. She watched him as he stood hunched at the phone, a rumpled mess, trying to calm his road manager down.

"Stop it!" he told the chattering phone. "It's okay. I'll get some sleep here." He turned toward Esther. "You or him?" he asked again. And, at Esther's perplexed expression, he added, "Your husband."

"I don't like the question," said Esther. Her directness and simplicity caught him off guard, and he could see the pain and vulnerability in her face. This was no girl to play games with, he thought. She followed a straight, honest path through life, calling her shots just as she saw them. He'd forgotten there were people like that.

"Mo'll take us to the airport, and you make room for us on the chopper," he told Ritchie, who'd gone on ahead to set up the gig. "I'm bringing somebody with me." He looked over at Esther.

"What's your name?" he asked her.

"Esther Hoffman." It's about time, she thought.

"Hoffman! Oh, Christ, I like that!"

"Why?"

"In the last year, you must be the only girl I met with a last name," he told her. "Well," he said to Ritchie with finality, "you tell him he'll have to send his chickie surface mail. I got somebody with me. I'll be there, Bobby, I'll be there. I'll be *there*," he promised, hanging up the phone.

As Esther brought in the pizza on two plates, John Norman looked around the 1920s sideboard that held condiments and candles, finding, to his relief, the remains of a bottle of wine.

"What went wrong?" he persisted, pouring himself a glass.

"With what?" asked Esther as she laid the place mats neatly on the small table.

"It's with whom. Your husband." Why did he want so much to know, he asked himself.

Why did he want so much to know, she asked herself. She hesitated, looking for the right words.

"He put mayonnaise on his liver and onions," she said. It was the only explanation she was willing to offer to this stranger, and it would have to do.

It would have to do, he thought. As he sank down on the old-fashioned sofa, John Norman felt exhaustion catching up with him. He fought it off, knowing that this girl wouldn't have any uppers; she probably didn't even know what they were. It was a struggle to keep his eyes open.

"Eat your breakfast," said Esther, pointing to his plate.

John Norman shook his head. "I told you, I never eat breakfast," he reminded her.

"What are you doing here, then?" It was a fair question, she thought. How come she was suddenly so vitally interested in the answer?

"Picking you up," he grinned. "Some raceway. . ." He waved a hand. "I got a concert."

Esther laughed at him, shaking her head no. "I'm not that kind of girl," she told him. She held up one hand, counting on her long, slender fingers. "First, we meet through mutual friends," she said mischievously. "You call me in a week, we—"

"It's this afternoon," he interrupted.

"You didn't even ask me," she reminded him pointedly.

She was so feminine, it blew him away! How come he'd never noticed that her eyes slanted upward? It gave her face a pixie look that was especially her own. Her eyes were as special as her voice.

"I swear I have the manners of a hog," said John Norman ruefully. "It'd mean a lot to me if you came." He looked at her seriously, discovering to his surprise that it really *did* mean a lot to him.

"Okay, I'll come." A simple, direct statement, just what he was learning to expect from Esther Hoffman.

John Norman raised his hand and reached for a curl of her hair, brushing it softly off her forehead. He'd been wanting to do that almost from the first minute he saw her. Startled by the movement, she pulled away, and a moment of embarrassment fell between them.

"What was he like?" asked John Norman softly.

It took Esther a second to realize that he was talking about her ex-husband. An expression of sorrow crossed her gentle face. "He wouldn't fight," she said.

John Norman shook his head gravely. "He wasn't for you. You like a fight." He glared fiercely into her eyes, like an angry tiger. "Less tenderness and more of the wild side!" He was kidding, but his act was convincing. Esther could see the power in his jaw and the strength in his shoulders. It frightened her a little. His eyes weren't mean, though. Crazy, maybe, and wild, but not mean.

"I can take all the tenderness you got, as a matter of fact," she said quietly.

"This wine has turned," John Norman said, changing the subject. This was getting a little heavier than he liked.

"I use it for cooking," shrugged Esther.

"Biscuits, no doubt," he teased her.

"I've got some Sterno," she teased back.

He grinned at her. She was a stone gas, he thought again. "Yeah, I drink too much," he conceded. "You change the subject too much. I guess they're both defensive measures. I'll take the Sterno."

"You're a mess," observed Esther, daintily picking up a pizza slice and taking a hefty bite out of it.

"I know, I don't cat right," said John Norman, watching her. "Peanuts, mostly."

The phone rang. Esther wiped her mouth and fingers with a linen napkin and ran to answer it. "Hello?"

"Put John Howard on," Ritchie's voice ordered her.

Furious, Esther barked back at the phone. "What the hell ever happened to 'Hello, I'm so-and-so, I'm sorry to bother you so early, but if you wouldn't mind' and so on?" she demanded.

"This is Bobby Ritchie, his road manager," said

the voice in a slightly more polite key. "Honey, he's got a concert in about six hours. Okay? So, can I talk to—"

"He's asleep," lied Esther, surprised at herself.

"Honey, you let him sleep," Ritchie cajoled. "What have you got there? Any coke, uppers, screamers . . . flush it. Just get him in shape to do a concert, we'll take care of you. Anything you want, understand? Anything. Money. A color TV. Whatever. . . Just get him on that chopper. . ."

Esther slammed the receiver down angrily. What kind of people were these? What was she letting herself in for? What kind of life did these people live if they thought that common decency had to be paid for or it wasn't forthcoming? Did they think she was some ordinary dumb groupie? Uppers? What were screamers? Coke? My God, did he do pills and coke as well as booze and grass? She fought to regain control of her feelings. John Norman wasn't like the rest of them. She knew that, was certain of it. If he were, he wouldn't be here in her apartment. For what did *she* have to offer a man like that?

When she'd regained her composure, Esther looked around for John Norman. He'd been prowling around her apartment, checking her out. Now he was holding in his hand some sheet music for the song she'd been writing. Her large blue eyes widened in alarm. These were her private things! Music was very personal to her; she didn't know whether she was delighted or frightened by a big musical star reading her music. Maybe a little of both.

"What's this?" he asked her. "This is the one you sang last night. You wrote it, huh?" He smiled at her broadly, tickled to death.

So he'd been listening after all! "Yeah," she confessed, nervous again and suddenly shy. "I only sing my own songs."

"Good," grinned John Norman, holding the sheets

of music out to her. "Pick one out and sing it to me."

"No, it's private." Esther shook her head, and her full lips set into a stubborn line.

"I'll sing it," offered John Norman.

"The hell you will!" The girl bristled like a cat. You could almost see her fur standing up.

"Then, sing it for me," he pleaded.

"I don't want to."

"What'd you write it for?" John Norman demanded. "You wrote a song not to be sung? You're kidding yourself. Here," and he thrust the music at her. "Sing it." He picked up her guitar.

"I don't play well enough," she demurred.

Taking Esther's hand in his, John Norman ran his practiced fingers over her fingertips. "You're not calloused enough yet," he told her. "We'll have to fix that. Sing."

"I can't . . . I'm embarrassed." The words came out in a near-whisper.

"I won't look," he promised her. "Go ahead . . . sing it." He turned his back on her deliberately, keeping his promise. Slowly picking up the guitar, Esther struck a chord, then another. Then she stopped, too nervous to continue. She sat on a chair, looking at John Norman's back until she understood that it was the sight of him that was making her so nervous. Turning her back to his back, she picked the guitar up again and began to strum.

"Well, listen . . ." she began, her words coming fast in her anxiety. "There really isn't a lyric . . . it's not finished yet . . . it's just an idea. If you don't like it . . . I want you to tell me."

"Okay," said John Norman from behind her.

"If you laugh, I'll kill you," she threatened.

"I promise. I won't laugh."

Esther began to play softly, humming rather than singing. The melody was sweet and lyrical, evocative of love and gentleness. The girl's sure, strong voice filled the room as she hummed, growing fuller and sweeter as she lost the sense of the man's presence and became caught up in her music.

Behind her, John Norman smiled, content. His senses were soothed and refreshed by this young woman's talent, beauty, and honesty. For the first time in a long time, he felt relaxed and at peace. He looked around the room again, digging it. He felt at home here. Stretching out on the couch, he pulled off his boots and closed his eyes, letting Esther's music wash over him. He settled down comfortably to listen.

Esther brought the song to a finish and waited. She wanted—suddenly she wanted very much—to hear what John Norman thought. After all, he was a professional, a star His opinion would be valuable, she told herself. But she knew it was something more than that, something other than a professional opinion she was waiting to hear. She liked this man, she felt drawn to him. Strangely, she felt that he *needed* her. She waited for his reaction.

But it never came. There was nothing but a heavy silence in the room, broken only by the sound of John Norman's regular, even breathing. Esther laid the guitar down gently, and stood up. She moved slowly to the couch and took a good look at John Norman Howard.

He was sleeping like a baby.

Chapter III

Esther had never been up in a helicopter before, and she found it both frightening and exhilarating. This was what it must be like going up in a balloon, she thought, being held aloft in a basket, swaying back and forth in the air. She had the feeling that whatever power was holding them up would let them drop long before they arrived at wherever it was they were going. She glanced over at John Norman, who had his head together with the other men in the copter. They were talking rapidly, going over tour plans, money, publicity. They were laughing and drinking together, but every now and then John would send a look her way to tell her that she wasn't forgotten.

So close to the ground, she thought. Like a bird. A bird's-eye view. She giggled to herself with excitement. Who could have imagined that little Esther Leona Hoffman, from the tiny town of New York City, would be riding in a helicopter with Mr. Rock-and-Roll himself! She still had no clear idea of how she'd got here, or even when she was coming back. It wasn't like her to be this impulsive. She must be getting young. And she laughed to herself.

Then Esther thought about John Norman Howard, and the laugh died on her red lips. Some day soon she was going to have to face up to, and deal with, her feelings for this man, so she'd better get it together. When she found him asleep on her sofa, she had felt a pang of disappointment, followed by a wave of sympathy. "I can't sleep," he'd told her, yet there he was, totally flaked out. She knew then that he was conquering his paranoia, letting his guard down with her. She had spent the next few hours quietly, washing her hair, doing her nails, getting ready for the concert. Still, she found herself returning to the sofa again and again, looking down at John Norman's sleeping face, trying to read him. She kept thinking: what drives a man to such unhappiness, such cynicism, such self-destructiveness? She'd heard a lot of stories about this man—that he was a boozer and a loser, that his band was slipping, that he screwed up his gigs, that he treated everyone around him, especially women, with callous indifference and even cruelty.

Yet, she felt none of this when she was with him. It was as though he had a secret reservoir of kindness, and he opened it only to her. He knew she was frightened of him, and he was quite obviously trying to show her that she needn't be.

But why me? thought Esther. What does he see in me? No, besides that, she told herself with red cheeks. I'm hardly his type; I'm not a groupie, I have no interest in making it with a rock-and-roll band. Even so, he had pursued her, first with cheap tricks and then, when he saw these wouldn't work, with a surprising gentleness and kindness. Was it only her music he was interested in? She didn't think so. What chord had she touched in him? More to the point, what chord had he touched in *her*?

Was it because she was not—unlike almost everyone else he encountered in the dogfight that was the rock business—just another star-fucker? Some rocker with a big-name band, she forgot who it was, had once told her at a party (told *her*, probably, because he was at first shocked, then fascinated by the fact that she was not interested in his body) that when he first went on the road with the band, he loved the fact that all these chicks wanted to fuck him. "Then I realized," he had said, "that all they wanted to fuck was my *name*, like a goddamn trophy. Didn't even wanna fuck *my* name, man, wanted to fuck the *band's* name."

She decided, while he slept, that she really liked John Norman Howard, scary mess that he was. Maybe something more than just liking, she didn't know. She was a little afraid to find out; afraid, too, of his instant, almost overpowering, attraction to her. Oh, well, she thought, take it slow, play it cool. Maybe she could help him a little. Watch the Jewish mother bit, Esther. Chicken soup can't cure everything.

The helicopter abruptly swung to one side and began its descent. She craned her neck to look down on the mob scene below: a huge sports stadium jammed with people. In the mammoth parking lot was a tiny white circle, toward which they descended. John Norman moved to her side. Grinning, he put his arm around her.

"We're gonna land *there*?" she asked.

"Uh-huh."

"In that little white circle?"

"Yep."

"God help us," she said. He laughed. A sudden rush of air caused her to turn. One of the men—it was Danziger, P.R. man for the Speedway—had opened the other door. "My God," she shrieked, "he's going to jump!" All three men yelled with laughter as Danziger showered the crowd with eight-by-ten glossies of John Norman and the band.

"Tell me again how you would like to slip in quietly and unrecognized!" she shouted over the roar of the chopper. He laughed and squeezed her to him.

The moment the copter touched down, John Norman grabbed her hand and threw open the door. "Keep your head down and stick with me," he shouted in her ear. They sprinted out from under the downdraft toward Bobby Ritchie, who guided them quickly between lines of policemen holding back screaming fans.

"Hey, mother," John Norman shouted to Bobby, slapping him warmly on the back. "This here's Esther!" Ritchie grabbed her and hugged her with genuine gratitude, his skinny face beaming. She was astonished.

"Thank you, Esther! God bless your little heart," he said, a grin splitting his face. They ran toward the open rear of a Cadillac ambulance where the rest of the band was waiting, all smiles. She had no way of knowing how amazed and grateful they were. Jesus! A chick had got John Norman Howard to a play date *on time*! Motherfuck, what next?

"Let's see what you got," a grinning Lee Dallas said as John Norman pushed Esther into the ambulance. The door slammed behind him and someone thrust an open bottle of Jack Daniel's toward his face. He took a long pull. Someone else passed a point. Everyone talked at once. "Hey, mother, where you been?" Much joking, backslapping, laughter. "What's happenin', baby?" "You up, man?" "I'm getting there; little more of this, I'll be there, man." "We gonna *rock and roll* today, motherfuckers!" Fans were beginning to rock the ambulance, but the police were fighting them off. John Norman leaned up into the cab.

"Hit the siren." The ambulance began its slow forward movement. Laughing, the boys in the band blew kisses at the hysterical girls running alongside. One girl ran with her face pressed to the glass, her nose pushed in, her features distorted.

"Looka there!" exclaimed Lee, and as they all howled with wicked glee, he leaned over and kissed her back through the glass.

Esther was speechless—half shocked, half thrilled, and totally bewildered. She watched carefully as John Norman got himself "up" for the gig, moving rapidly into a stoned, hypertensive state, and farther and farther away from her. He was like a very fine, tautly stretched piece of wire, trying to see just how far he could extend himself before. . . It was exhilarating and hypnotic and frightening and sad, all at the same time. An uncontrollable shiver ran through her body. What was she doing here?

"Thought we lost you," Lee said to John Norman as the ambulance nosed its way out of the last remnants of the crowd and the band settled down a little.

"Hell, no!" John Norman's voice was unnecessarily loud; he was very high now, and speeding. "I like bein' a rock-and-roll star, always with a happy smile on my face."

During the short drive, Ritchie and Danziger had been putting their heads together in whispered conversation. Now Danziger leaned back from the jump seat up front and tapped Esther on the shoulder. She turned quickly, a little spooked.

"Esther, isn't it?" he asked. "I'm Gary Danziger, John Norman's P.R. man." His voice had an oily quality that Esther hated instinctively. "Bobby Ritchie told me about you. This is Pumpkin," and he pulled the underage groupie closer to him.

Esther couldn't resist. "Oh, is your last name Pie?"

"You see me after the show," Danziger continued. "I wanna fix you up, okay?" He smiled a P.R. man's smile. John Norman caught the expression, but not the conversation. He knew that look and didn't like it. Frowning, he took another slug of Jack Daniel's.

The ambulance whipped into a curtained-off area that was the backstage and came to a stop. Everybody piled out and rushed into the frenzied activities of concert preparation. Everybody except Esther.

Bobby Ritchie stuck a pass on her sweater and planted her in what he hoped would be an out-of-the way place, where she stood—wide-eyed and open-mouthed—watching what appeared to be bedlam.

Ritchie began shouting instructions to the swarm of roadies crawling over, under, and around the monstrous sound and light system. Masses of wire and cable were everywhere. The band, still drugging and drinking heavily, began to change into their costumes and tune their instruments. Esther, having been immediately uprooted from her assigned spot, found herself moved to another, only to be uprooted again. She stood clutching her purse, gazing upon this madness. Every once in a while, John Norman would shout and wave to her, grinning. God, she looks fabulous, he thought. She was dressed in a cable knit white coat sweater over jeans. A matching knit cap was pulled down over her curls. The outfit and her dazed expression made her look for all the world like Little Girl Lost.

The noise and confusion heightened with each passing minute. The huge crowd roared out front; pandemonium reigned backstage.

Groupies, roadies, and the press milled about, apparently to no purpose. Security was particularly heavy today, including even a group of bikers, their cycles parked neatly in a row next to the ramp. Esther, remembering Altamont and the Stones, felt the hair on the back of her neck stand on end. Danziger walked by, moving her once more. "Excuse me, sweetheart," he said, and started off.

"Pssst," she motioned him back. "Are those Hell's Angels?"

"Not quite *that* heavy," he said, and was gone.

She was uncomfortable, not wanting to be in the way, not wanting to be noticed. But she was absolutely fascinated by the frantic buildup of energy and concentration. The band began to tune up seriously. She could *feel* the tension they gave off, especially John Norman, who began his manic pacing and tuning, pacing and tuning. Nicky Fiedler positioned himself behind his trap set, flexing his powerful shoulder and arm muscles, giving short bursts of warm-up rim shots and paradiddles.

"You didn't give us the set yet," he said to John Norman, who paced in front of him, head down over the Gibson Firebird, whipping the cord behind him at each turn. John Norman looked up, his face twisted in anger and tension.

"We been doing the same fucking set for eighty-six straight days now. I thought you had it down." He spat out the words, his concentration broken.

Ritchie was watching the crowd, gauging the moment. As the roar grew to a frantic pitch, he turned to check the band.

Esther felt funny, queasy. This is creepy, she thought. What's the matter with me? Then she realized that she was afraid. John Norman took another drink, looked at her, and smiled wanly. He seemed to recognize her, but from very far away.

"Ready?" Ritchie barked. They all nodded. "Now!" he screamed, dropping a raised arm.

A mass of fireworks exploded, creating a curtain of multicolored flame and smoke in front of the band as they ripped into the low-down boogie called *Hellacious Acres*. The crowd went bananas.

John Norman smiled as he hunkered over his guitar and commenced an incredible solo riff that brought him nearly to his knees and back up again. As the solo built, the crowd became wilder and wilder. For him, it was like a fix, like the highest of highs. He moved from Dallas on bass to Pete on keyboard, playing off each one, throwing the solo back and forth.

Nicky humped his drums like a madman, head down, driving hard. Moving center stage, John Norman turned his back to the audience, spread his legs wide, and started hump-hopping backstage toward Nicky in the old fifties Bo Diddly style, also known as fuckin' the axe, each jump punctuated by an earth-shattering chord. Nicky, head up now, hair flying, grinned insanely and executed a daringly high-speed but flawless series of rolls from snare to tom-toms to cymbals and back again. The crowd was completely out of its head. Esther was mesmerized. The John Norman Howard Speedway was hot today, and when they were hot, by God they were the meanest, best goddamn rock-and-roll band in the world!

Backstage, Bobby Ritchie and the stadium owner and the promoter stood around a table on which were spread a couple of loaves of Wonder Bread, a plate of cold cuts, a jar of mayonnaise, and several six packs of beer. Bobby picked up a limp slice of balogna, held it above his head, and let it drop to the table, a look of utter disgust on his face.

"This isn't Nova Scotia salmon."

"I don't get your point," the owner said evasively.

"Our contract calls for Nova Scotia salmon," Ritchie said sternly. "Our contract calls for three cases of domestic beer, three cases of Seven-Up. . ." Warming to the litany, he ticked off each item on his fingers and bit off every word. "Three cases of canned Coca-Cola, twelve bottles of wine, Bolla Soave and Valpolicella—two gallons of bottled water, one gallon of orange juice—fresh. . ." Esther, who had moved backstage to escape the mind-numbing roar of the music and crowd, walked into this scene and was dumbfounded. My God, she thought, is it worth it, being a star? Is this what it meant? Cold cuts?

Later in the set, she returned to the ramp, heading to the stage to watch John Norman. He and the band were still going strong, stripped of much of their clothing now, sweating, drinking, and playing hard.

She had seen and heard a lot of rock-and-roll in her short life, and this was some of the best. Even though it wasn't her cup of tea.

John Norman was crooning a love song now, looking at her, singing to her, his eyes wild and crazy, but a beautiful smile on his face. She smiled back at him, blowing a kiss. But she was troubled. Something is eating him up, she thought. He looks . . . like he might explode. Just blow sky high and take all of us with him.

John Norman keep looking at her, never taking his eyes off her throughout his solo. I think I'm in love with her, he kept thinking. I love her, love her, love her. His mind reeled from the drugs and the music and the crowd. Love her, love her. So good. Such a good person. So nice to me, even a shit like me.

Laying down his mike, turning the solo over to Lee, John Norman strode toward Esther, staggering a little, grabbing a bottle of vodka and a fresh towel on the way.

"Come on out," he said, offering his hand. "I want you to see how it feels in the lights." She backed away, laughing nervously, afraid he would pull her on stage.

"There aren't any lights."

"You want lights?" he asked. Turning, he threw his head back, shouting at the top of his lungs.

"Give her lights!"

Esther continued to back down the ramp, shaking her head. He followed, a manic smile on his face, his eyes burning into her.

"The sun's out," she said nervously.

"Turn off the sun and give her the pink spot!" he shouted. They were at the bottom of the ramp now, where a melee of groupies, cops, bikers, deputies, and hangers-on had gathered to see what was going on.

"Don't miss this, honey," one groupie whispered

to another. "It's flip-out time for John Norman again."

Danziger and Ritchie cut their way through the mob as a giant biker—hair in a greasy pigtail, leather jacket with the sleeves cut off, eye patch—grabbed John Norman and kissed him on the lips while administering a bone-crushing hug.

"What are you doing?" Bobby demanded. John Norman was still in the biker's grip, his feet off the ground, that crazy grin still on his face.

"Courting Miss Hoffman, Bobby—okay by you?"

"Oh, man, you're beautiful," the biker said, setting John Norman down. "I love what you do, man." They stood in front of the row of motorcycles.

"I love your Harley, man," John Norman said.

"It's yours. I mean it's yours, you're beautiful."

Now John Norman was surrounded by shouting, grabbing people. Ritchie, cursing, dreading another aborted concert, was furiously trying to get him back on stage. He and Danziger had just agreed that the tour couldn't stand another fuck-up when they had been summoned by John Norman's shouting.

John Norman, searching for Esther, finally spotted her standing to one side. "Hear that," he shouted at her, leaping on the big Harley—crazy now, a man possessed. "I'm beautiful. He loves me. You love me. We'll go for a ride." As he kicked the starter of the huge machine, Ritchie and a couple of cops ran forward and tried to pull him off. The biker would have none of it.

"Back off, leave my man alone, you fuckers," he shouted, punching out a cop.

"You're going to kill yourself!" Esther screamed as John Norman roared up the ramp toward the stage, laughing hysterically, accelerating wildly. As the bike hit the top of the ramp it soared a few feet into the air, scaring the band. They ran for cover and the crowd went crazy as John Norman, obviously out of control, tried to dodge amps, speakers, instruments. Then he attempted a trick few skilled dirt bikers can manage: sliding the bike in a circle while still astride it, but keeping one foot on the ground. That failing, he leaped off the bike, kept his hand on the accelerator handle and described a circle around himself with the motorcycle at high speed. Esther stood at the top of the ramp with the others, horrified. They were all—Bobby, Danziger, the cops—too scared to go near him. The crowd, not certain whether this was part of the act or not, cheered, applauded, laughed, and jeered.

Suddenly, John Norman tried to jump back on the speeding cycle. As he hit the seat, it shot straight into a giant tower of speakers and amps. The tower tottered a moment, then cascaded down upon him.

Pandemonium broke loose on the stage. Esther screamed and ran toward him, only to be held back by security guards. She struggled, but was shunted aside with the others. "Please, please," she begged. In a blur, she saw Ritchie moving toward the motionless body with a doctor. "Hey . . ." she pleaded. But Ritchie didn't seem to recognize her. He pushed his way through and squatted next to John Norman. Medics were unfolding a canvas stretcher. John Norman grabbed the front of Ritchie's T-shirt, trying to pull himself up.

"Where is she?" he said. Ritchie was relieved. At least he wasn't dead.

"You take it easy, John Norman. There's no blood. You'll be okay. Jesus, *why*, baby, why do you have to do it?"

"Where the hell is she?" John Norman growled. "You fuckin' find her, Bobby."

"Yeah, yeah, it's gonna be okay," Ritchie said. "You lie back now. Take it easy. These boys here'll get you out." The medics lifted him carefully onto the stretcher and carefully bore him through the mob, Ritchie and the security men cutting a path before them. Again, Esther tried to reach him. She had to see him, to comfort him. No use. They wouldn't let her near him. She broke from the crowd and rushed to the helicopter, but hundreds of fans were already there, pushing and shoving against the tight circle of cops.

"Let me through," she kept repeating. "I know him, he needs me. Please!" She saw Ritchie moving into the chopper with the stretcher. She shouted and waved, crying hysterically now. He didn't answer.

The helicopter pulled up and away. The cops began clearing the crowd. Esther stood alone in the vast lot, her head thrown back, watching the sky long after the chopper had disappeared, carrying John Norman with it.

Chapter IV

John Norman Howard winced in pain. He hurt all over. His sprained and bandaged right hand hurt. His cracked ribs hurt. His pulled leg muscles hurt. The numerous bruises, the two small broken bones in his foot, the knots on his head, everything hurt. Need more medicine, he thought, and began to paddle slowly toward the bar at the edge of the swimming pool.

John Norman was lying on his back in a small rubber raft, floating in the middle of the Olympic-size pool behind his palatial Italianate Hollywood mansion. He was dressed only in a pair of jeans and a few Ace bandages. Members of his band and crew were playing frisbee on the lawn.

The giant swimming pool was leaf-strewn and filthy. Weeds pushed their way through the many cracks in the concrete apron. The wrought-iron lawn furniture was rusting away; the cushions were faded and losing their stuffing. The half-dozen potted trees were all dead; the curtains over the once-elegant cabanas hung in shreds, and dozens of dirty glasses and empty liquor bottles were strewn on every table. It was the day after the outdoor concert and the "accident." A heavy pall of depression hung over everything and everybody. Bobby Ritchie stood frowning under the ripped and faded canvas canopy that overhung the dilapidated bar at one end of the pool. With him was his secretary, Sunny, a cold but efficient girl in her late twenties. She wore rimless spectacles, a tank top, and a long skirt. In her arms she was cradling a stack of mail, phone messages, lists, and schedules. Over her shoulder hung a tote bag full of notebooks and a tape recorder. A terribly thin, sexless young man with longish hair lurked around her. He was dressed in a leather suit on this scorchingly hot day. He was her boyfriend. Nobody could figure that one out. Sunny was reading off the call-back list.

"Mister Blau of Smith, Grunwald, Pennybaker and Funk called on the fifth, again on the seventh. A Miss Hoffman, Mister Blau, a Fred Simpson—said he'd call back—Miss Hoffman again, a hang-up, Maggie Abbott, Miss Hoffman again. . ."

"All we want is the business stuff," Ritchie cut in. "Tell Blau I'll call him later. It's about the Detroit Grand Jury number."

"What about—" Sunny began.

"Forget the junk calls, okay? Matter of fact, let's change the phone number again." That'll get rid of the little bitch, he thought. Trying to suck around John Norman. Fuck her! Fuck Esther Hoffman!

Somewhere a radio was playing. The announcer rattled off the day's ration of bad news: mass murder in Fresno, CIA assassination attempts, FBI cover-ups. As he paddled about with one hand, John Norman softly sang, "I love you, Suzie Q. . ." I should have been an Everly Brother, he thought. Life was simpler for an Everly Brother, wasn't it? Fuck the seventies, let's bring back the fifties.

John Norman managed to reach poolside. Ritchie was there with a fresh Bloody Mary, holding it out like a reward.

"You go to her place?" John Norman asked.

"Who?"

"Esther."

"She wasn't home."

"Son of a bitch. Why doesn't she call me?"

"I don't know, John Norman," Bobby lied. "Maybe she's out of town. What's she got the other two thousand ex-cheerleaders didn't have this year?"

"I don't like that, Ritchie."

"I'll cut my tongue out."

John Norman gave his roadie a hard look. Then, quickly grabbing an ankle with his good hand, he toppled Ritchie into the pool. Bobby came up sputtering and cursing as John Norman paddled away, laughing. He lay back and floated, eyes closed to the bright sun, thinking.

Goddamn shit! Where the fuck could she be? Why won't she call? Sure I fucked up again, but if she'd just give me another chance. . . Blew it again, John Norman, you hopeless flaming asshole. She was the best thing to happen to you—the first woman who didn't con you—in months. Years, maybe.

Years, yes. How many years had he been living like this, surrounded by money-grubbing ass-lickers and brainless star-fuckers? Not many, really, but it seemed like always, like it was always this way—cold and lonely and always moving, never settling down, never falling in love. Never really *making* love. Oh, he'd screwed his way back and forth across the country plenty. But when was the last time he really looked at a woman's face, told her she had a beautiful mouth, touched her hair? It seemed to him that every time he had felt moved to make a gesture of affection, they always said some stupid thing, like "Who're you taking to the Grammies this year?" or "How much money do you make?" or "Why don't you buy me a car?" Hell, when was the last time before Esther he'd had a *conversation* with a woman?

He guessed the last woman he could recall really

caring about was Darlene. He chuckled to himself at the memory. Good old Darlene. Wonder what happened to her after Ann Arbor? Rock-and-roll had taken over his life; what overtook hers? Probably lives in some Detroit suburb, he thought, with a mess of kids and a good husband who works for Ford. That would satisfy Darlene. That's why he lost her.

He thought about his childhood, growing up in the expensive Detroit suburb of Bloomfield Hills, and how much he had hated it. His father was a successful CPA, a hard-working, nice man, an ineffectual father where John Norman was concerned. He was more interested in Russell, John Norman's older brother and the embodiment of the upper-middle class values he had spent his life striving for. With Russell, he could bury his own Kentucky farmboy origins. Russell became the varsity athlete, the Prom King, the class president, the Most Likely to Succeed. Russell had manners, knew how to dress and to talk. Took up golf and played with his father. Russell was a CPA now, too. He was also, in John Norman's eyes, an asshole. It was he who, when John Norman's career really began to take off, wrote that "polite" letter suggesting that his dearly beloved brother adopt a "stage name," so as to spare the family any possible embarrassment.

He suspected his mother was behind that one. Dear Martha Lou, that blue-grass bitch. Unlike her husband, she had come from "good" family. Kentucky blue blood. Somehow—John Norman could never figure it out, given her calculating mind—she had married beneath her. Which was why, he supposed, they lived "up North." It was she who really ran the family. That meticulously clean, suffocatingly "decorated" house, the country club membership, the right parties with the right people. She was a hell-for-leather Junior Leaguer, liked to get up at five in the summer and hit the first tee by six. Once a week, the family got dressed and went to dinner at "the club." John Norman hated those club nights. No matter what clothes he put on, she always made him change something. Throughout the meal, she corrected him constantly. After dinner, his parents always lingered over coffee, greeting friends, being seen, while he squirmed helplessly in his chair until his father released him with the words, "John Norman, go play by the pool."

He didn't think Martha Lou Howard really *hated* him. She just found him . . . well . . . embarrassing. He had been a quiet kid—not a recluse, just quiet. He had friends, but as far as she was concerned they were the wrong kind, though their families were as Christian as his own. The difference was that their fathers worked in factories and belonged to unions. Most of their parents were from the border states, like his own, having come north to work in the factories during the war. But they still sounded like it, still loved the country music, still held on to a piece of the South in their lifestyle.

So did he. He spent every minute he could in their homes, which were much more congenial than his own. Often, his friends' parents would have to send him home. When his mother was really angry with him, she used to shout, "John Norman, you talk like trash, you look like trash, and you spend your time with trash!" White trash. That was what she saw him turning into, and it made her sick.

As a teenager, he recalled, she nearly had heart failure when she discovered he was secretly racing stock cars. When he turned sixteen, his father had offered to buy him a new car. He said he wanted an old car. His parents thought he was crazy, but he said he was into fixing up old cars. They relented, and he had soon found a dream of a '57 Ford to rebuild. His mother would not allow him to work on it at home (the vision of an old car up on blocks in the driveway was for her the ultimate white trash nightmare), so he did it at a friend's house. She found out he was racing the day he walked into the living room of their spotless home, blood dripping from a nasty gash in his arm, haphazardly bandaged with a grease rag. He said he'd had an accident, but he had actually totaled the Ford at the drags, and when she found out, she was livid. He was still convinced that the real cause of her anger was the blood he had dripped all over the pale yellow wall-to-wall. The stains never did come out.

John Norman had been an indifferent student, but in 1962 he entered the University of Michigan at Ann Arbor. The first year he spent most of his time at the campus's wildest fraternity, from which he was finally expelled for refusing to move from a tree-house he had built in the frat's backyard. He taught himself guitar and piano that year and started —with a lot of other freaks—to hang out in the rockabilly bars and clubs that were mushrooming up in the area. Occasionally, he would jam with one of the several freak bands that were forming around that time, playing the music he loved—fifties rock and straight country—but he didn't think of himself as a musician. Others who did valued him for two things: he was a whiz at repairing instruments, and he had a great ear for other people's playing. And of course they liked him for his easy-going almost country manner. Most of these young musicians were Eastern, many Jewish, others just plain Middle Americans with no roots or traditions. John Norman, however, was a real "Michigan hillbilly." Those were the days, he thought—the music, the dope, even the politics. The feeling of *belonging*. He was twenty-four. God, twenty-four!

"There he is!"

The voice startled him out of his reverie. He raised his head to see Brian Wexler, his personal manager, Gary Danziger, his P.R. man, and Freddy Lowenstein trooping across the lawn, followed closely by his business manager, his lawyer, and his investment counselor. Invaders with their news of the real world. The men were all dressed in expensive business suits and ties; Freddy was in one of her over-priced Rodeo Way pajama outfits, her neck and wrists dripping gold jewelry. She was a middle-aged Jewish Princess who had successfully been around Broadway, the movies, fifties pop, and now, rock-and-roll. Her style was pure Polo Lounge phony, but she had a razor-sharp wit and the mind of a banker. Freddy was a lawyer and a good one, but now she owned and published a rock-and-roll tip sheet. It was a powerful force in the industry.

"Hello, darling!" she shrieked, a forced smile on her makeup. They were all forcing smiles and pretending great good humor. In fact, they were all scared shitless. Their little gold mine was no longer producing, and none of them had the vaguest idea what to do. They had planned this day's invasion in the hope that they could jolly their star into bailing himself and them out. It had all been going so well; what went wrong? What did he want? They *had* to find out, *had* to make him happy. Surely the ride couldn't be over already.

"God, how beautiful!" Freddy gushed. "Look at the birds! Brian! Where do they come from?"

"Terrific!" Danziger said pointlessly. The others greeted their meal ticket effusively. "John Norman!" "Glad to see you, John Norman." "Glad you could see us, John Norman." He stared at them indifferently, then began to paddle over for a fresh drink. He would need several, he knew.

"Look at him!" Brian announced, spreading his arms above his head. "Jesus, he looks *wonderful*! We work our asses off in an office, and he lives like a prince!"

"You'll have the tan of the town, my sweet!" cooed Freddy. John Norman dragged himself out of the pool, grabbed his crutches, and hobbled to the bar for vodka. The rest of them stared after their wounded warrior, pained expressions on their faces.

"He needed that. It's a good thing," Brian said to the others in a low voice.

"Hear me, my loves," Freddy said sarcastically, "Brian's trying to turn this into a plus."

Moving to a grouping of chairs and tables at one end of the pool, the financial cadre settled down, flipping open attaché cases, pulling out pocket calculators, financial statements, computer read-outs—the toys that made them feel competent to solve any problem. Brian grabbed for the telephone; Danziger began to attack "the problem" of yesterday's concert.

"We give it dignity," he said positively. "We plant a story with *Time*, the *New York Times*. Not just the rock creeps."

"Thank you, Gary," Freddy said, with a killing look.

"How about something simple, like nobody was killed?" Brian said. Then, into the phone, "I'm with John Norman Howard, what's doing?"

John Norman hobbled over with his drink and flopped down on a chaise. They all stared at him. He still had not said a word. Now he closed his eyes, trying to remember the name of the band he first went scuffling with on the road. The Noble Five, that was it. Shit. The Noble Five—what a name! He had dropped out of school by then, and his parents had cut him off. But he had gotten into repairing and rebuilding amplified equipment, and was making a nice living off local musicians. He had his own apartment in Ann Arbor, where he lived with Darlene, a sweet-faced, plump girl from Ohio who had picked him up in a bar one night. Darlene wasn't too bright, but she was sensitive to his needs, loved him, and left him be.

The Noble Five was made up of some dropouts

turned musicians, plus a couple of older guys who'd knocked around the Detroit music scene. They started out playing any date they could get—teen dances, after-hours bottle clubs, blind pigs, hillbilly bars—and they could play *anything*. None of them knew much about how to repair equipment, and they really had to spend their time concentrating on the music. They all still worked full time then, saving money to buy a better sound system. They knew they didn't have their own sound yet, but they knew they were good, and they had high hopes. One of them, Lee Dallas, even had ambitions as a songwriter. The memory of that made John Norman smile.

When they started, he remembered, they had come to him for help. All they had were little Fender amps plugged into microphones, and everybody played into one amp. After a while, each had his own Marshall amplifier, except Lee, the bass player, who had a Sunn. They would tell John Norman how much money they had and the kind of sound they wanted. He would buy the equipment and show them how to use it. He began to go out on dates with them, packing the equipment in his station wagon, setting it up, going through a sound check with them, then knocking it all down afterwards and hauling it home. Soon they had two Fender guitar cabinets and an amplifier to plug their microphones into. John Norman started building PA cabinets. He learned all this from playing guitar and keyboards, fixing his own organ, reading the trades, experimenting, and—as they traveled more widely—talking to other groups. It was through these out-of-town dates that he learned the most. He bought an Econoline van to truck the equipment in, usually made the motel arrangement (his only rule: find the cheapest place in town), collected and disbursed the earnings. He even discovered that there was a name for what he did. He was a "roadie." As the Noble Five gained a regional reputation, John Norman became an invaluable part of the group: travel arranger, truck driver, banker, keeper of the stash.

But it was his skill as a musician—though he often jammed with them, he never performed on stage—coupled with his technical wizardry that was his greatest asset. Lee or one of the others would say, "I'm looking for this type of sound," or "I need this, I think I'm going to try this," and he would put things together for them, experimenting with this or that piece of equipment. They were a very picky bunch, but he kept them happy. Occasionally, one of the members would drop out, to be replaced by another musician, usually selected by John Norman. When he first began to work full time with the Noble Five, he did it on the basis that when they made some money, he made some money. Everything they did or had was shared; they ate the same food, slept in the same room, made the same money. Since he was handling the money, he was really paying them. They never really understood how completely he controlled them. But *he* did.

And he kept them straight. He was a stickler for getting to a date on time; he insisted on a complete sound check with every member present before each performance. When they graduated from the Econoline to a Ryder rental, John Norman drove it. He dealt with the hassles: the messed-up hotel reservations, the blown fuses, broken drumheads, groupies who stole, rental problems in a strange city when you've got no credit cards and nobody wants cash. He learned how to deal with union labor, and what to do with nonunion labor (watch them like hawks; if they're not stoned, they steal)—in short, John Norman took care of everything.

After every gig, they would drill him, demanding to know what happened on each song. During a performance he would be checking lights, securing wiring, adjusting amps, doing his thing. But he was also listening, and they knew it. Lee, especially, interrogated him. "Well, how was I?" he would say. Did you hear any words I could take it easy on?" or "We got lax; don't you think we got lax?" They became very close on the road, Lee and John Norman. After a gig, the band would all go drinking, but he and Lee were always the last to fade. They would drink and talk music for hours, finally staggering to bed singing old fifties rock favorites.

One night, at the tail end of a Midwestern tour working as the opening act for a second-rate group that Columbia had signed for peanuts and was trying to launch for peanuts, the two of them were getting quietly stoned in a spade dive in Toledo. They were taking turns feeding quarters into a jukebox full of vintage R & B classics. They were both very drunk, feeling no pain.

"Ya know, Lee," John Norman said, "this ignoble Noble Five of ours is goin' nowhere fast."

"Shit, man," Lee said, "we're doin' all right."

"You call twenty-eight days on the road out of thirty all right? You call sleepin' in fleabag motels all right? You call scufflin' for every goddamn dollar backin' up second-rate groups with recording contracts while we got none all right? I call it *shit*. You can spend the rest of your days livin' like this, old buddy. I ain't."

Lee took a long pull off his drink and thought a minute. He took a long sideways look at John Norman.

"What you got in mind?" he asked slowly.

John Norman leaned back against the bar, staring at the ceiling. From the box, Little Anthony and the Imperials were wailing "Tears on My Pillow."

"I got in mind scuttling the fucking act. Startin' over," he said. He turned to Lee and looked him straight in the eye. "You know, Lee, the best fuckin' musician in this band don't even play with it." He paused and smiled. Lee remained silent. John Norman turned and signaled the bartender for another round. "Now, you're a pretty good musician, Lee," he said, turning back, "but the rest, well, let's just say they're doin' exactly what they oughta be doin' and what they're likely to keep on doin' the rest of their lives." He put down his drink and grabbed Lee's jacket, gripping it tightly, his voice intense. "But not me, baby. Not on your life. I'm gonna make it, and I'm gonna make it big," he said, "I'm sick of dickin' around in honky-tonk clubs, travelin' second class, watchin' no-talent assholes go to the top. It's *my* turn, goddammit!" He was almost shouting into Lee's face, his voice rising in anger. He loosened his grip and smiled again, turned away, and took a slug of whiskey. Lee hunched over the bar and stared into his drink.

"John Norman," he said slowly, "I been watching you run this band quite a while now. Been noticing, too, how you just sorta took over everything." He looked up. "You know," he continued, "we always like figured this band didn't have a leader. We were all equal, everybody sharin' everything, the work and the money." He stared at John Norman, who didn't speak, and then Lee turned back to his drink. "But I guess that just ain't gonna work, is it, John Norman?" He looked up. "I guess somebody's got to be the leader, somebody's got to be the star," he said. "That's just the way this fuckin' world works, ain't it?" He smiled. "But then, I guess you already figured that out, didn't ya, good buddy?"

John Norman grinned back broadly. "You bet your sweet ass I have," he said. He'd figured it out a long, long time ago. Had always known it, planned it carefully, paid his dues and more, learned everything he could about the business—more than all the others, more than anybody had to. Because he knew that to make it you had to do it on your *own*, man! You're all alone in this crummy world. If you aim for the top, don't trust anybody to put you there without getting paid for it.

That had been his rule of life, John Norman thought now, stretched out on the chaise, and he had stuck to it religiously. He had made it. He was the biggest. And goddamn it, he thought, remembering that conversation in Toledo that started it all, he was still the best. You fuckin-A. The best.

"John Norman, dear boy, are you *listening* to this?" Freddy's voice shrilled at him. All of them —Brian, Freddy, Danziger and the others—were slumped in their chairs, coats shed, ties loosened, their business toys spread out before them. Brian paced about, on and off the telephone. Danziger was tickling and whispering to his groupie, who giggled constantly. It was blazing hot, and sweat poured from all of them.

Lee Dallas wandered over from the frisbee game with Ritchie.

"When Brian says he's cancelling the tour he doesn't mean it in a pejorative or punitive way, sweetheart," Freddy said, wiping her brow.

"It'll be John Norman's decision," Danziger put in. "He'll announce it to the press."

"What?" Lee bellowed. "You cancel us out? What are you saying?" Brian turned abruptly from his pacing and hung up the phone.

"I'm saying the tour's a disaster," he snapped. "I'm saying promoters won't take the shit, the late starts, the damages to the halls, the legal hassles. Somebody has got to be realistic."

"Succinctly put, Brian," Freddy said from behind closed eyes. Her mascaraed eyelashes fluttered.

"Twenty-seven thousand dollars deducted for vodka. Eleven thousand for orange juice," the business manager interjected, looking up from his computer print-outs.

"The man likes screwdrivers," shrugged Danziger.

Brian had been staring at John Norman in exasperation. The star had still not said a word and the manager was getting fed up. He turned his anger on Danziger, a favorite target.

"Why don't you go get laid?" Brian barked. "It's been almost three or four hours—"

"Okay," cut in the business manager. "Then there's the tax lien."

"What are we talking about in that department?" Brian asked.

"About in the area of one hundred eighty-six thousand, six hundred fifty-four dollars and thirty-two cents. Some area!"

"The man has to make three times that to pay it off!" Brian fumed. He began to pace again, waving his arms in the air as he spoke. "He's got fifty percent going out for taxes! By the time he's paid his agent's fee, the business management, dues, expenses, etc., etc., what has he got, maybe a fourth of what he takes in, if he's lucky. What the fuck does the government want from him?"

"Four grand in bail money just to get out of Detroit," Danziger murmured.

John Norman still had not opened his mouth. He lay propped on his elbows on the chaise, looking from one member of his staff to the other, his face a mask. Slowly, he rose and hobbled to the edge of the pool and stood for a moment, his back to them. Then he fell forward limply into the water and swam slowly away. They all looked after him wordlessly, then back at each other. Brian began to pace again, exhorting his troops.

"I feel this negativism withering every creative idea," he intoned. "We've got to stop '*no*,' try to feel '*yes*'. Otherwise," he continued, turning back to them, "we get nowhere."

"Beautifully said, Brian," Freddy remarked, not taking her eyes off John Norman, who floated on his back in the pool, his eyes closed. "Inside, he's thinking," she announced. "John Norman goes inside, it's meditation. He'll come out with an answer." She paused, then jumped up from her chair. "God, this sun, it's like hammers, I *love* it!" She moved into the shade of a tree.

A helicopter could be heard approaching as the others resumed their argument. Brian moved to the edge of the pool and paced the apron beside John Norman. He was rapidly losing his temper. The helicopter came closer, and Brian found he had to shout over the noise to reach his apparently indifferent star.

"I've had inexhaustible patience," he yelled. "I've kept my temper. I've left you alone to do exactly as you want." John Norman did not look up, did not even open his eyes. The whir of the helicopter filled the yard. It was coming on, flying low. "Now you've got to help," Brian said, screaming to make himself heard. "I can book you into the Indian Relief Benefit—if you can get there on time."

The helicopter roared into view, coming in very low over the back yard, hovering. A shower of leaflets fell over the lawn and into the pool. The propwash blew the leaflets around in little cyclones, and the downdraft scattered business papers everywhere. The leaflets announced radio station KARE's "All-Time Top Forty Weekend. Forty-eight hours of the Top Sound on the Top Station." Some of the band and staff picked up copies to read, then threw them aside. They went on shouting at each other over the noise. This sort of dumb thing seemed to go on all the time.

A bunch of leaflets hit John Norman in the face, and he blinked to attention. The pool was covered with floating pieces of paper. He looked up. The copter was holding directly overhead. Someone crouched in the open doorway with a bullhorn.

"John. . . Norman. . . Howard," the amplified voice boomed down, "an oldie but a goodie on

K-A-R-E! Fifty thousand watts of KARE power!" The noise was deafening. Everyone stared at the copter. John Norman began to swim to the side of the pool.

"John Norman," the voice from the copter continued, "this is your numero uno fan, Bebe Jesus!" The name came out, "Bay Bay Hay-*soos*!"

John Norman, angry now, laboriously pulled himself out of the pool.

"Bebe Jesus want you to come down and rap with us on our All-Time Top Forty Weekend," the voice continued, "three of which are John. . . Norman. . . Howard platinum platters. . ."

John Norman moved as quickly as he could to Mo, who sat coatless in the sun, a pistol exposed in a black shoulder holster. John Norman grabbed the pistol, aimed at the helicopter, and fired wildly. The sound of the shots was lost in the copter noise.

". . . played by Bebe *Jesus*!" the freaky amplified voice went on. "Hey, don't shoot, Big John, we're on your side." John Norman fired again, aiming better this time.

"Crazy asshole fired on me!" the voice of Bebe Jesus shrieked. "He hit us? What the fuck? I'm all right! Hey, John Norman, you think you're getting on my show? Not *once*! Forty-eight fuckin' straight hit-makin' hours and not *once* will I mention your name, shitface!" The copter turned abruptly and pulled up and away. John Norman stared at it grimly, still holding the pistol.

Ritchie grabbed the phone and dialed frantically. "Very funny, John Norman," he fumed, "a very funny number."

John Norman did not reply. Instead he hobbled in the direction of one of the cabanas.

"It's inhuman what we ask these people to do," Brian clucked, shaking his head. "They're in a pressure cooker, night and day."

"Police?" Ritchie said into the phone, "I want to

report a sniper . . . yeah, sniper. An unknown person who shoots a gun. . . correct. Somebody fired at us. . . Two shots."

John Norman Howard stood in the front of a mirror in the cabana, the pistol still in his hand. He looked intently at his face. He did not like what he saw.

Chapter V

"Rolling," the voice boomed from the control booth, "take six."

Esther stood with her group, Phyllis and Sydelle, in an audition studio at Station KARE, the station that cares and rocks-and-rolls you. They were taping a commercial spot—for a cat food called "Meow Chow." It was the sort of anonymous work their agent managed to get them now and then. They hated it, but it paid the rent. They stood facing the control booth window, behind which stood an unhappy director and advertising man. The session was not going well.

There had been five takes already, none of them exactly right. Standing in front of three mikes, the girls heard the instrumental track through the earphones and they began the lyric as the director cued them:

"Meow
For Chow
Like little kittens do
Meeow
The chow
That kittens love to chew

And now we're proud to say meow
Announcing something new
We bring you now *mature* Meow
Old cats have feelings too
Meeee-ooow

Esther cracked up on the last line; she couldn't stop giggling.

"No, cut! Cut!" the director screamed. "That's a retarded ending. God, I hate amateurs."

"You mean the long meow at the end?" Esther asked

"Yeah. You, the one on the right. You with the kinky hair?" He was pointing to Esther. "You're too strong, anyway. Can you pull it down some?"

"Sure," she said. "I'm really sorry, I just—it's very peculiar, y' know? One more time, okay? We'll get it right."

"Okay," the director said. He turned to the ad man in the booth with him. "We got the first part, let's do a pick-up." He opened his mike. "Girls, we've already got the first part, let's just pick it up from 'kittens have to chew'."

"Kittens *love* to chew," the ad man said. "*That* kittens love to chew."

"Yeah, yeah, *love* to chew. Y' got it? Okay, Meow Chow cat food commercial, take seven." They tried it again:

And now we're proud to say meow
Announcing something new
We bring you now *mature* Meow
Old cats have feelings too—

Esther cracked up again. She couldn't help it; the line destroyed her.

"Old cats? You sure you wanna say that?" she asked.

"Yeah, honey, we're sure."

"We can't waste time on this," the ad man said. "Get rid of them."

"It was funnier the second time," Esther said.

"Okay, girls, take ten. Let's try to pull ourselves together," the weary director said. He switched to public address, over which the station's current on-the-air program could be heard. It was Bebe Jesus and his All-Time Top Forty.

"I'm allergic to cats, anyway," Esther pouted, removing her headset. But she was upset. Pissed off, really. Fuck him, she thought. Fuck you, John Norman Howard, Rock-and-Roll Star! Drop dead, you creep. She'd been trying for days to get him out of her head. After the freak-out at the stadium she had made herself sick with worry. Was he okay? Was he hurt bad, maybe dead? She had phoned him at his house, his office, everywhere she could think of. No word. When she heard over the radio that he was all right, she started to get angry. Angry at him, but angry with herself, too, for caring. Yes, she knew she cared about him, knew he had touched something in her that nobody had touched since her marriage. And that scared her. Because she knew he was crazy as hell.

"Whatsa matter with you?" Phyllis demanded, moving to Esther's side.

"I always laugh when I'm sad," Esther said. She looked up with a weak smile.

"Forget him," Phyllis said. She knew where Esther's head was. She was also street-wise enough to know it was no good. "Honey," she warned, "he never had a woman he didn't send away screamin'."

"What?" Esther said. "Who told you that?"

"Nobody tol' me. I read it. At the checkstand at the supermarket."

"He's not like that," Esther retorted feebly.

"He's a star. They're not like people."

"Of course he's people. At least for a minute

there, I thought he was." Hell, she thought, why defend him?

"What do you wanna do?" Phyllis asked. Esther was lost in thought.

"I don't know," she said in a sad voice. Then she looked up, brightening. "You wanna go eat a lot of chocolate?"

Phyllis laughed. "Girl, you kill me," she said, and they began to gather up their things. Esther moved to the window and gazed out at the heat rising off the parking lot pavement. A man limped toward the building, lugging a heavy square box in front of him.

"Phyllis!" Esther screamed, her eyes widening with recognition, "you're never gonna believe this!

John Norman moved purposefully through the stifling heat toward the KARE studio. His bum leg ached. The case of Jack Daniel's Black Label Tennessee Sour Mash sippin' whiskey weighed a ton. Christ, he thought, the shit they put you through. Now I gotta kiss that greasy little fucker's ass.

He slammed his way through the front doors, past the open-mouthed security guard, past the rows of secretaries who looked up aghast, past the station manager's office and directly into Studio A. Everybody knew about the shooting incident, and word spread quickly through the station that John Norman Howard was there with a peace offering.

Wearing doubleknit jeans and a giant gold crucifix, Bebe Jesus sat in the glass-enclosed broadcast booth, the big, double-turntable console in front of him. Stacks of records and tapes surrounded him. He was on the air, his mike open, his hand poised on a record.

"And now, gang, get off on this fabulous, fabulous piece-a music from nineteen sixty-seven, the Beach Boys!" As he said these last words he looked up and saw John Norman enter the empty studio. Instantly,

Bebe jumped up, switched off his mike, and let the record roll. He was freaked.

"I got a phone here," he said over the intercom as John Norman approached the glass with the case of whiskey. "I can have a cop here in a minute."

"I'm sorry," John Norman said, his voice flat.

"Who gives a rat's ass?" Bebe shouted. "You took a shot at me, my lawyers are talkin' about it! I don't want it!" He pointed at the whiskey. "I don't want your bribe, man! What the hell is that?"

John Norman shrugged and turned. He'd tried. Now Ritchie couldn't say he hadn't tried. As he walked away, Bebe cut the Beach Boys off and went on the air.

"Hey, you know who just walked in here, his hat in his hand?" he said into the mike, his voice jaunty, but with an undertone of sarcasm.

John Norman stopped in his tracks.

"I don't mention his name on the air," Bebe cooed, "but his lawyer just told him he better get on the right side of Bebe Jesus, because Bebe don't take no jive from burned-out superstars."

John Norman stood about ten feet from the booth, his back to it, his head thrown back, his eyes closed. His breath came rapidly, in deep gulps.

"This man," Bebe went on over the air, his voice rising in anger, "let me tell you this man's ego! He has fallen from the firmament, man, and the wonder of it all—why, I looked up in the night, and I don't see no hole, I don't see nothin' missin'. I see so many stars I can't count. Who needs *him*!"

"I said I'm sorry, man," John Norman said through gritted teeth.

Bebe cut off his mike. "Hey, man," he said standing up and pointing at John Norman through the glass, "get that shit, whatever it is, outa my studio. I don't take nothin' from you, because you are a rude and joyless burned-out, spoiled pain in the ass. We're *bored* with you, man!" He was screaming now, his dark face screwed up in rage, his mustache quivering.

Slowly, John Norman turned around, his handsome face grim. Slowly, he lifted the heavy case of Jack Daniel's over his head. He hurled the case directly into the plate-glass window, straight at Bebe's head.

The window shattered into a million splinters. The impact slammed Bebe back into the control panel at the back of the booth. Records, tapes, and costly equipment went crashing to the floor, taking Bebe Jesus with them.

His rage spent, John Norman limped quickly out of the studio and toward the front of the building. Nobody came near him. They didn't dare. They had all heard what had happened, since whatever is said in the on-air booth is piped through the building. As he walked past Studio B, he caught a glimpse of Esther, standing open-mouthed, staring at him. Esther! He swerved toward her, struggling with the massive glass doors, trying to get at her. I don't believe it, he thought. I don't believe it. What is she doing here?

Esther saw him coming and, in a panic, began to gather up her things, looking for the exit. She had to get away from him, and fast, because he was plunging along, coming straight at her like a Navy destroyer. Trembling, she shook her head in dismay. Trouble, she said to herself. This man is trouble wherever he goes. She wanted no part of him.

It was too late. He was in her studio now, limping toward her. Had that damned motorcycle crippled him for life? He looked haggard, she thought, haggard and uncared for. No, she wasn't going to give in to thoughts like these. Screw him, he deserved whatever he got!

"Where'd you go?" demanded John Norman, grabbing her arm.

Esther pulled away from him. "Everywhere you

go," she said coldly, "fighting breaks out and things get broken. Have you noticed that?"

"I called you about eight times," he told her roughly, ignoring her sarcasm. "How come you never called me?" His eyes drilled into her, burning her face with the intensity of his gaze.

"I did try. Three times. The fourth time I got a disconnected number."

"What do you mean?" John Norman's brow creased in puzzlement. Then he slapped a hand to his forehead. "Oh, Jesus! Hey, what's the date?" He looked at Esther in distress. "They changed the number. . . I forgot the date. . . Every six weeks they change the number," he babbled, "because I get these kook phone calls. . ." He broke off, aware that it sounded like the phoniest bullshit rap of all time. How could he convince this girl that he was telling the truth?

"Yeah?" said Esther, eyeing him in evident disbelief. "Well, listen, I'm glad you're okay. Lots of luck, all right? I think you need it." She turned to go, and when he grabbed her again, she froze him with a look. John Norman let her go, realizing that he was coming on too strong. As soon as he released her, Esther vanished through the doorway, leaving John Norman to hobble after her, yelling, "Wait a minute, will you?"

"No. It'll never work," she said, not missing a step. "I'm a nonviolent person."

"We got a million things to talk about," he protested.

"I don't think so." Esther shook her head with finality.

By now they had come to the end of the corridor and were stopped by the elevator door. Esther pushed the button firmly, her face averted, determined not to look at John Norman. His face would only get her into trouble.

"I can't handle it all by myself," he was pleading,

begging with his eyes. "You could've reached me. I'm easy to reach. You call my public relations man. He calls my agent. My agent calls my business manager. *He* calls my personal manager, who calls my secretary, who makes a list of who called. She puts it in a green alligator folder and they give it to me every other Tuesday."

The elevator arrived and Esther stepped into it, followed closely by John Norman, the self-mockery still on his rugged face.

"Which you never open," remarked Esther bitingly.

"Which I give unopened to my public relations man," agreed John Norman.

"To handle," retorted Esther, suddenly rather enjoying the game.

"Today is my birthday," said John Norman.

"What?" He had taken her completely by surprise. She didn't know whether to believe him or not.

"I can't handle it," he grinned. "Let's run away. Meet my mother. Marry me."

"Sure," said Esther, trying to keep her cool. "Maybe when you need a tambourine I get to shake it."

"Esther . . . Esther . . . I want you. . ." John Norman pleaded as they left the building and walked onto the sunny street.

"Is today really your birthday?" Esther turned to face him head on.

"You just changed the subject," grinned John Norman sheepishly.

"Listen, honey, if you don't want to go, *I* will." Esther turned to find Phyllis laughing at both of them. Esther smiled back at her friend, then looked speculatively at John Norman, making up her mind.

"Okay," she nodded finally. "Where's the hearse?" She looked around for the Cadillac and Mo.

Suppressing a laugh, John Norman pointed to a little red Ferrari, sitting by the curb in a no-parking zone. A parking ticket was stuck under the wipers. "I bought it because it looks like you," he told her proudly.

Puzzled and more than a little suspicious, Esther followed him to the car and climbed into the passenger seat. But when John Norman pulled the parking ticket from under his wipers, shredded it, and threw the shreds to the four winds, Esther found herself laughing with pure pleasure. She might live to regret this, she told herself, but she knew for certain that if she didn't go with John Norman Howard now, she'd regret it all the rest of her life.

They sped up Angelo Drive, winding up into Beverly Hills. The wind tugged at Esther's curly hair, blowing it back off her face. John Norman drove very fast, just as she'd expected he would. He was half in love with easeful death, she thought, picking a scrap of Keats out of her high school memories. She shook the thought out of her head; she certainly didn't want to deal with *that!* Life was her bag, not death.

They rounded a curve, and Esther saw a huge estate, fenced in by a large retaining wall topped by electrified wire. A massive iron gate, flanked by two large stone lions, guarded the property from lesser mortals and predators. John Norman braked to a stop in front of the gate. It remained closed.

"Damn it! This car doesn't open it!" he complained, frowning. He rummaged in the pockets of his Levi's for a key, finding it at last in a jacket pocket. Pushing open the car door, he got out and inserted the key in one of the gateposts.

"One of the privileges of wealth?" asked Esther as the gate opened smoothly.

"This car hasn't been keyed into the system yet, that's all. It's too new," explained John Norman, climbing back into the driver's seat.

They drove on through the gate and up the circular driveway, going fast. Suddenly, an alarm bell rang shrilly, and a pair of attack dogs, looking to Esther as big and as fierce as saber-tooth tigers, came racing to the side of the car, barking savagely. The Ferrari was open and low to the ground. Esther felt the dogs' hot, fetid breath on her face and realized that there were advantages to large, closed cars, advantages she'd never before considered.

"My God!" she exclaimed breathlessly to John Norman. "You *like* living like this?"

"Like what?" John Norman honestly didn't know what she meant.

As they pulled up to the house, Mo ran out to shoo off the dogs. He ran with that curious combination of grace and waddle that fat men often manage surprisingly well, and he made good time. In his hand, he carried an electrified cattle prod that the huge Dobermans were obviously wary of; they loped off around the house. Esther had a thoughtful expression on her face as she stepped out of the Ferrari.

She found herself staring at the opulence of the giant mansion that rose before her. It reminded her of old photographs of the pleasure palaces of the 1930s, when cheap Depression labor and low taxes had combined to bring to the newly-rich of Hollywood a grandiose standard of living not matched since. The gardens of John Norman's house were a riotous mass of colored blooms, giant palm trees, and fountains graced by stone statuary. The red tile roof, Spanish style, dipped over tile-encrusted Moorish arches. Hearst would have felt right at home here, she thought. Why bother traveling north to San Simeon?

Esther watched him as he unlocked the front door and ushered her inside, past stone angels that reached their alabaster fingers out to her from either side of the massive wooden door. She followed him into the great hall, her blue eyes widening in astonishment. She had never been inside such vast empty spaces, not even at Grauman's Chinese. It was the largest house she had ever encountered, and it was almost totally empty of furniture. Esther was afraid to raise her voice, certain that the place would echo.

"How many rooms are you crammed into here?" she asked.

"I don't exactly know," John Norman admitted, giving a little shrug. He followed Esther into the gigantic living room, watching her in amusement as she wandered about, open-mouthed. Long, elegant draperies hung at the windows, left behind by the house's original owner, but there were no other touches of grandeur in the room. It was not totally bare, but it seemed so to Esther. Amps and speakers, a grand piano, a Moog synthesizer and console, and a worn sofa were the room's only furnishings. Big as the sound system was, it looked like a set of child's building blocks on a nursery floor.

"This is a funny place," Esther said. She tiptoed onto the bare floor and unable to resist, took a long slide on the polished wood, as delighted as a child. John Norman couldn't help grinning.

"I still haven't got it together," he told her.

Esther looked startled. "You planning a skating rink here, or what?"

"I mean, the acoustics aren't right yet."

"This is wild!" exclaimed Esther, swooping around the vast room. "You could throw your own block party indoors." She wrinkled up her nose at the mouldering food containers and Schlitz cans that littered the floor.

"We record in it," called John Norman from another room.

"Well, as long as you're having fun in it . . . otherwise, I'd get rid of it . . ." She went off in search of John Norman, following the sound of his voice.

He was in the game room, and Esther paused in the doorway to catch her breath. Her eyes widened as they traveled around the room; here was a fortune in electronic games and toys for rich kids: Pachinko, electronic basketball, electronic Ping-Pong, a video strategy set, a pool table, a dart board, a pinball machine—even a one-arm bandit, in front of which sat a giant plastic Hefty bag filled with nickels, so that you didn't have to use your own money to play. It was Disneyland for freaks, a paradise of conspicuous consumption for people with nothing important to do.

"They tell me it's an investment," John Norman shrugged.

"When you want to eat, you . . . uh . . . just order in some deli . . ." said Esther in distaste, waving at the rotting food cartons.

John Norman poured himself a large vodka from the bar in the corner. Esther hadn't seen so many bottles since her rich cousin from Westchester married the dentist. She stood at the pool table, playing idly with a cue, as John Norman approached her, carrying his drink.

"Chinese takeout, mostly," he answered her question.

Every time I see him, he's carrying booze, she thought. Every goddamn time. "Are you an alcoholic?" she asked him suddenly.

John Norman blinked. He'd never thought about it. "Probably . . ." he began slowly.

"You could have used some vocational guidance," she told him, anger darkening the blue of her eyes.

"Why? What's wrong with me?"

Esther waved a hand at him in exasperation. "You're living in a million-dollar slum!" she ranted. "Why do you do that? What were you? Rich? Or poor?"

John Norman was tickled. If she didn't like him, she wouldn't be yelling at him, he reckoned. "You're cute," he told her.

At the limit of her patience, Esther stalked out. John Norman sprinted after her. "Who are you,

Esther Hoffman, and where did you come from?" he yelled into the echoing hallway.

Esther was scouting the rest of the house. She peered into the long, formal dining room. Empty. "So many rooms . . . this is a great house for people who never want to see each other," she snorted, heading for the stairs. "Where are the phones? No phones?"

John Norman tried to explain. "There's one out by the pool in case I need it . . ." he began.

"I just happen to love it when the phone rings."

"You won't love it so much when they call you up at four in the morning, and someone you never heard of is telling you he's full of Quaalude and he's got a gun and you're the only person in the world who can tell him why he shouldn't use it," said John Norman morosely. Idly, he picked a can of spray paint off the top of a packing crate and wrote "Esther" on the wall—backwards. It was an old trick of his; he hadn't thought of it in years.

"Why do they call you?" asked Esther, trying not to show her pleasure that he had written her name, or her horror that he'd mutilated the lovely wall.

"Because they love my music," John Norman replied with a short, self-mocking laugh. "They think I got all the answers."

"You don't?"

John Norman shook his grizzled head. "I don't even understand the questions," he told her ruefully.

The master bedroom lay off the gallery at the top of the stairs. It was dark; the heavy velvet draperies were pulled across the long windows, keeping the room at constant midnight. Esther started to draw back, but John Norman moved quickly to the windows and pulled back the curtains, letting in the strong sunlight. The room was, of course, huge, and the only object in it was a waterbed mattress sitting on the floor, without its supporting frame. It was covered, more or less, with a messy pair of satin sheets, rumpled and rather stained. Esther approached the bed gingerly, threading her way through the beer cans and food cartons which littered the floor here also. Stretching out one foot, she prodded the mattress with her toe. Like a sleeping monster from a dark lagoon, the mattress stirred, undulated, and gurgled.

Both of them stood there, saying nothing, the sexual tension thick between them. Esther thought with sudden longing of the grand piano downstairs—safe, familiar, and precious.

"Who cleans this place up?" she asked, turning away from the bed.

"I don't know."

"You don't know!" She couldn't conceive of such a thing. Not to know who was responsible for your property?

"My manager takes care of it," shrugged John Norman. "I'm always on a plane. Too many takeoffs, too many landings, too many places I didn't want to go. I been on too many planes."

"I've only been on two," said Esther, relieved that the subject had been changed. "Wait! Is a helicopter a plane?" she asked him.

John Norman let out a delighted roar of laughter. "I got to teach you *everything*," he said. "You only been on two planes, and you think you got the answers for everyone." He came up to her, standing at her shoulder and looking down at her with pleasure written all over his face. He lifted one hand gently and touched her hair again. He'd never get tired of touching her golden curls, he thought. There was so much life in her hair! It seemed to him that her hair represented Esther herself . . . warm, alive, glowing, brilliant in color. Or was it her mouth? Or her eyes?

As she felt his fingers on her hair, Esther looked

up into his face. "How many names you painted around this place?" she asked. Then she walked out of the bedroom.

John Norman realized suddenly what was bothering Esther, why she was giving him such a hard time. "One," he said as he followed her out of the bedroom and down the stairs.

She moved gracefully across the living room, not sliding like a kid, and sat down at the piano. Her fingers brushed the keys lightly, then began a melody new to John Norman. He listened in silence. She was much better at the piano than at the guitar. As the melody unfolded, filling the room, he poured himself a tall vodka and came up behind Esther. She appeared to be lost in her music, in a world of her own making, but John Norman knew that the girl was acutely aware of his presence behind her.

"That's nice," he commented softly, as she finished. "What is it?"

"I keep thinking it's going to be a sonata when it grows up."

"It would make a terrific song," he suggested.

Esther shook her head. "It goes too high. Nobody can sing it."

"Play it again," urged John Norman. "Real sweet, like you did just before."

Esther went back to the beginning of the sonata, feeling it flow under her fingers. To her astonishment, John Norman began to improvise a lyric, humming and singing. "Time has come again . . ." he sang, "and love is in the wind. . ." The words felt good; they fitted perfectly.

Esther stopped, her hands frozen on the keys. "Oh, that's so good!" she cried. "But I'm getting lost in you and I'm forgetting how my song goes. . ." She turned to the piano again, picking up John Norman's line and singing it herself, but he was suddenly there next to her, taking her fingers off the keys and kissing them one by one, and Esther knew with a painful beat of her heart that the time was now for both of them, that there was no escaping it any more, not now, not ever. None of the words that she knew could change things, none of her good sense would come to her aid now. Lost, she told herself. I'm lost in you. Save me, she begged. I don't want to love you. I don't want to love an alcoholic, a crazy man, a man who is half in love with death. But even as she said these things to him silently, she knew that it was too late . . . too late.

She felt her hands reaching up to cup his face, felt the wiry strength of his beard, the hollows of his cheeks, the burning of his lips. And then his lips were on hers, snuffing out her resistance, his tongue forcing her mouth open, and then . . . oh, then her mouth opened gladly and accepted his. Oh, yes! she thought. Oh, yes! I want to love you! I want to love you now!

Pulling her up from the piano bench, John Norman clasped her tightly against his body, hurting her. But she gloried in the hurt, in the strength of his arms. She needed a strong man. Please, God, let him be a strong man! She felt him lifting her up—how strong he was!—felt him carrying her across the room. She was light as air, light as a dandelion seed, just drifting across the room. She felt giddy, potential, a kaleidoscope of brilliant, fragmented feelings. Somewhere, buried deep, was a flame, a little flame that was growing bigger every minute, that was getting ready to consume her. Oh, yes, she thought. I want to be consumed. Eat me alive. I need to be devoured, to grow like a baby inside of you, John Norman. Take me inside you.

There was a pile of soft, large pillows in one corner of the echoing room. It took them a year to get there, but at last, his mouth still on hers, John Norman laid Esther down gently on the pillows. His lips traced a path of warmth and chill from her mouth to her brow, and down her cheeks to her throat. Everywhere he kissed her his mouth left an imprint that said "John Norman." She felt his hands at her breasts, gentle and insistent at the same time, and she arched upward so that he could reach them more easily.

Under her hands, his hair and beard were filled with his energies. She couldn't help touching, stroking—it was like the fur of a large cat. She had never made love with a bearded man before, she thought suddenly. God, it felt good! In the same moment, she was seized with the crazy desire to lick his eyelids, to feel his lashes against her mouth, and she moved her lips up his face until she felt his lids under them. The tip of her tongue snaked out and slid along his eyelids. . . Esther felt John Norman's head move in sudden astonishment, and then he laughed. Nobody had ever done that to him before. They were even; she'd never felt like doing that to anybody before. It was wonderful, though. Maybe they'd stumbled onto something. She laughed along with him.

The sun poured in through the openings in the draperies and fell in bars over the polished floor. Esther felt the warmth against her skin, the warmth of the sun and of John Norman's hands, and realized drowsily that part of her was bare. Not enough . . . not enough. Raising herself suddenly from the pillows, she moved over John Norman, pressing him backward until she was sitting on top of him, smiling down into his face. With one single, graceful motion, she pulled the silk shirt off her body, baring her breasts as a gift to him. The pleasure in his eyes as he looked up at her made her smile; it dispelled her shyness and filled her with a surging abandon. I've had lovers before, she thought, but this one is different . . . he's different. He's the part of me that has been missing and I never knew it.

And then they were naked, both of them, he pulling her down to his body so that the softness of her lay full length upon the hardness of him. She cried out once as he entered her, because of the goodness, the rightness of it. It seemed to take forever, their lovemaking—there was no beginning to it, no ending. It went on and on, carrying them higher and higher, past pleasure, past sensation, and into pure feeling. Esther fantasized: first, that they were the only two people in the world. This room, this vast, high-ceilinged room, was the world and they were lost somewhere deep inside it, the only two people in existence. Next, that they were one person, only one and not two, each of them contained in the other, so totally intermingled that there would be no separating them, ever. I am John Norman and he is me, she thought. As different as we are, we are one and the same person. When he left her at last with a groan of sated pleasure, she felt as though he were still with her, and she clasped his sweating body in her arms, fulfilled.

As for John Norman, he was blissful and at peace. He could not remember a time when he had been able to relax after sex. He had always had the urge to put on his pants and go out into the night, ready to booze and to boogie. The girl was an appetizer, and the banquet lay elsewhere. But it wasn't that way with Esther. He lay in her arms feeling at one with himself and the universe, feeling in touch with the core of himself. With them, sex was only the beginning. He shut his eyes and he slept; he had come home.

And after a while Esther slept, too.

They woke up several hours later, at almost the same instant. The sun was setting, and the shadows were long on the wooden floor, reaching for them like dark fingers. They laughed a little, a bit shy with each other now (when was the last time he had been shy with a woman? He couldn't remember). Picking their clothes up from the floor, they wandered naked through the house like two children, winding up in the bedroom.

John Norman laughed at the expression of distaste on Esther's face as she regarded the messy bed. When he brought back fresh sheets, he was tickled to see that she had picked up all the mouldering food cartons and the beer cans and tossed them into a litter bag. While she made the bed up, John Norman took the garbage downstairs. How domestic, he thought, and grinned.

When he returned he saw that she had pinned up her hair, and for the first time John Norman saw the back of Esther's neck. It turned him on, the sight of her neatening up his bedroom, wearing one of his huge T-shirts, lost in it. He felt a new surge of desire take hold of him.

"Hey . . ." he called to her softly.

"Can I help you?" She put on her best stewardess coffee-tea-or-me smile.

"Yes, you can help me," he whispered huskily as he buried his face in her hair. "I think you're the only one who *can* help me."

They made love again, on the waterbed, giggling and rolling. It was Esther's first time on a waterbed, and she kept complaining that she was getting seasick. This was something new to John Norman, this mixture of passion and laughter, and he was surprised to find himself really digging it. This affair was turning out to be full of surprises, and so far, they'd all been pleasant ones.

I'm going to keep a record of every time we make love, thought Esther. No, forget it. I'd rather lose count.

The second time was different from the first time. They were easier with each other, more relaxed and familiar. The undulating motion of the bed freaked Esther at first.

"I don't want a piece of furniture doing it *for* me," she grumbled, making John Norman laugh out loud. But she soon got used to it and, later, she even got off on it. "Still," she said afterward, "I think I prefer a bed that stays in one place. I feel like we shoulda had a bon voyage party."

"Oh, we did, we did," murmured John Norman, his face between her breasts.

"I'm sticky," Esther announced. "I need a bath. Which way's the john?"

"We both need a bath. I'll join you," John Norman said.

He padded across the room and got the bathroom ready, refusing to allow Esther inside until he was prepared. Then he stepped back, watching for her reaction. It wasn't long in coming.

"What is this? A shrine? This is the only religious bathroom in the world!" she shrieked, gasping at the dozens of candles that stood on the floor, ringing the deep tub. The scent of the hot wax was sweet, redolent of bayberry, and bubbles were piled high in the tub. It was an environment; John Norman had created a private world here with his candles and—Esther howled with laughter until the tears ran down her cheeks. The candlesticks were beer cans, dozens and dozens of empty beer cans.

"It's environmentally sound," said John Norman proudly. "Recycling."

"Beautiful," murmured Esther. "The only form of ecology that comes with its own hangover."

They sat facing each other in the tub, knees pressed together, soaping each other solemnly. "And I thought that nothing beat my rubber duckie," sighed Esther as John Norman painted a mustache and beard on her face with soapsuds.

Hugging and kissing, they played in the water like a pair of young otters, splashing the floor and each other. When the water cooled, they let it run out, but John Norman filled the tub again, reluctant to put an end to their games. Rummaging around the bathroom, Esther found theatrical makeup and rock star glitter, and she brought it back with her to the bathtub.

Once again they faced each other while Esther, frowning in concentration, stroked John Norman's cheeks and brow with paint and carefully applied glitter and rhinestones. When she had finished, she looked at him. He was a stranger, a gaudy, satanic stranger and, for one long moment, she felt a thrill of fear. Then he smiled at her, and it was John Norman again, and she wanted him. She reached out to touch his body, to stroke it and tease it, and feel it respond to her touch with a rigid urgency of its own.

When he took her again, she cried out in wonder that she could have lived twenty-five years without him.

Chapter VI

Esther lost count of the number of times they had made love. The days passed so quickly, and the nights so slowly. They went to Disneyland once, and once they drove up the coast to San Francisco, stopping at every inn and motel that captured their interest. They ate at the best restaurants and at taco stands; they went to invitational previews and drive-in movies. And they always had the same conversation.

"Move in with me, Esther. Come and live with me."

"I can't, John Norman. I can't live the way you do."

She spent many nights in his house, but she always went back to her little bungalow on Orchid, to her own space. She needed an environment that she created for herself—neatness, order and beauty.

And one day John Norman understood what she couldn't tell him. He hired a team of heavy-duty cleaners, and they arrived with industrial vacuum cleaners, and scrubber-polishers. When they left, the huge house glistened. John Norman called Esther on the phone and asked her to come over.

"Well?" he said as she walked from room to room, smiling, the smell of fresh wax tickling her nose.

"Well?" she retorted.

"Move in with me, Esther."

"I thought you'd never ask, John Norman."

Their days together took a new turn—furniture-hunting. If anybody had told him six months ago that he'd enjoy it, he would have laughed. But Esther made it fun.

First of all, she hated department stores, preferring instead the small antique shops on Little Santa Monica and Melrose, where she picked out comfortable, beautiful things one at a time, and bargained for better prices. The dealers grew to recognize her and, after a few weeks, to save her the best of the new shipments. Slowly, the big house began to take on the characteristics of a home. Plants bloomed indoors, and gently faded, good Oriental rugs made oases of softness on the hard floors. John Norman discovered that he no longer had the urge to use the floors as litter bins. He loved having the sheets always clean and sweet-smelling; he enjoyed the fresh fruit from the Farmer's Market that Esther stocked the refrigerator with. He even learned to drink orange juice, although he spiked it with vodka, even at breakfast.

They grew toward each other, like vines whose roots intertwined deep in the same soil. They talked a great deal, telling each other—slowly at first, then with a rushing of words—the stories of their lives, their earlier loves. No two people could have come from more different backgrounds than they; they had different families, had been raised in different faiths, possessed different mind sets and outlooks. Yet they felt sometimes like the two sides of the same coin, and John Norman was often convinced that Esther could read his thoughts.

They were lovers; they were friends. They spent their nights with one another's bodies and their days with one another's minds. Esther left her singing group, and Phyllis and Sydelle came to the big house on Angelo Drive for lunch. They all cried and hugged each other, and promised always to be friends. John Norman talked to Ritchie and Brian and Lee on the telephone for hours at a time; the Indian Relief benefit concert was very much on his mind. But he never wanted to rehearse, not even when the others would come to the house.

It wasn't like the old days with the Speedway. John Norman was different, more subdued, a lot less of a hell-raiser. The house and Esther made the guys uncomfortable somehow, as if they were afraid to put their feet up, and Esther sensed this and kept out of their way. She had no wish to butt in on John Norman's thing, because she had something of her own.

It was their secret, Esther's thing. Esther's songs and Esther's voice. John Norman knew that she could be a star, a great star, one of the brightest, and he was determined to see her up there—to push her up there himself, if necessary. What he wanted was an album, Esther's album. He intended to produce it himself, bringing to bear all his technical expertise and his instinctive musical genius, and to use the Speedway as Esther's backup. He hadn't told the guys yet, but he knew he'd have to tell them soon. Meanwhile, he drilled Esther like a top sergeant.

"Start over, you're losing it," he told her firmly. "Punch it in."

Esther looked up from her guitar. The back of her neck was aching; they'd been at this for hours now. "You want to make me a machine?" she complained.

"I want to make you a perfectionist," he grinned.

"I'm already a perfectionist," she retorted, raising an eyebrow.

"Running in and picking up the bath mat every time I take a shower doesn't count. Come on, do it."

Esther bent her head to the fretboard again. "You noticed that, huh?" she said softly. It gave her a warm feeling that John Norman had noticed the bath mat. She sang the first line.

John Norman switched on the Sony. "Again," he

ordered as he adjusted the mike to pick up her voice at optimal range.

Esther obeyed. She sang the line again and again and again, all at John Norman's orders.

"Okay, that's feeling good," he told her at last. "Try two lines."

Sighing, Esther muttered into the guitar strings, "I also wash out your hairbrush."

It took John Norman three weeks to get Esther ready to go into the studio, but the record didn't come together as soon as they'd hope. Part of the trouble was John Norman's fanatical perfectionism where Esther was concerned; it made him order take after take on every song. Part of the trouble was the Speedway. They had some difficulty adjusting to Esther's sound. They were, after all, a rock-and-roll band, and rock and roll was as far from Esther's music as a bull elephant is from a kitten. But mostly, it was Esther herself. Sensing the tension between John Norman and the Speedway, sensing the race against time as the costs on the album mounted sky-high, Esther became nervous, and her nervousness cost them more time and more money.

But it went even deeper than that. Esther had her own ideas about her own music, and they often differed from John Norman's. She respected his musical taste and his judgment, but that little voice inside her, the one she'd obeyed all her life, told her that her way was better. Yet, she couldn't bear to hurt him. Aside from her deep, growing feeling for him, he was spending all this time and money on her. She didn't want to appear ungrateful and stubborn, yet . . . it was, after all, *her* voice, *her* music, and *her* album. All of these mixed feelings led to irritating delays.

It was Ritchie, of course, who voiced everybody's impatience to John Norman. It was always Ritchie.

"What the hell am I supposed to say to Brian?" he

hissed. "You already ran up three weeks of overtime on this album. The guys have a beef, and I think it's a legitimate beef." He glared at John Norman, who avoided his look, gazing instead at Esther, who sat behind the thick, soundproof glass of the recording studio. She wore heavy earphones and an expression of concentration, and she was singing. John Norman couldn't hear the music and she couldn't hear him and Ritchie.

"They say the tour was shit," continued Ritchie, laying out the Speedway's grievances. "The music is old stuff you rejected for old albums, and where's your new stuff? Now you want to record the chick."

"Can she sing?" John Norman interrupted proudly.

Bobby waved one impatient hand. "She can sing," he admitted grudgingly, "but she's not our sound. The Speedway is better than backup for a pop singer. They got their own sound."

A look of guilt and embarrassment came over John Norman's face. "Hey, I didn't know they felt like that," he lied. "They don't like her?"

"I didn't say that," Ritchie scowled. "I said, she's got your head all fucked up." A sound behind him made both men turn. Esther had left the control booth and was standing in the doorway. John Norman searched her face for some sign that she had been listening to them, but her expression was one of worried concentration; it was obvious to him that her mind was on something else.

"John Norman? Look, I'm really grateful . . . they know so much," she said in a hesitant voice, biting her lip. "But I have to do it the way I hear it in my head . . ."

Behind her back, Ritchie grimaced in irritation. This broad was already telling the Speedway how to play! Where the hell did she get off? John Norman must be out of his gourd; Bobby had never seen him pussy-whipped before, and he didn't like it.

"What's wrong?" John Norman asked her.

Esther tried to put it into words. "They go . . ." she dooh-dahed a rapid tempo, snapping her fingers quickly. "But it should go . . ." and she changed the tempo, bringing it down and giving it unique little twists. "How do I tell Lee?" she asked, looking earnestly at John Norman. "I feel like a fool."

"That's *good*," said John Norman enthusiastically, picking up on Esther's revised tempo. "Let's try . . ." Humming it, he took off for the control booth to talk it over with Dallas. As Esther turned to follow him, she caught Ritchie looking at her with narrowed eyes. It wasn't hard to read what he was thinking. Taking a deep breath, Esther decided to stay behind and face him.

"I'm not bad for him," she said quietly.

"He's not working." Ritchie shook his head.

"He can get through a day without getting drunk, and he can sleep without downers."

"He's not working."

Esther opened her mouth to say more, then closed it again. How could she reach this man? She knew that she couldn't. Sadly, she turned and followed John Norman.

Ritchie stood looking after her, his face a study in dislike mingled with worry. She was right; he knew she was right. John Norman was looking better than he'd looked in years, rested, younger. Healthier. And Esther had done it. But where did that leave the Speedway? Or him, Ritchie? Shit, John Norman could get healthy as a horse, but horses don't sing. And horses don't make money. Shit.

The song was cooking now, growing organically into something unique and beautiful. Esther could feel it, feel that it was right and good, as right and good as her feelings for John Norman. "Evergreen . . . time won't change the meaning of one love . . . ageless and evergreen."

Love soft as an easy chair
Love fresh as the morning air
One love that is shared by two
I have found with you

Like a rose under the April snow
I was always certain love would grow
Love ageless and evergreen
Seldom seen by two

You and I will make each night a first
Every day a beginning
Spirits rise and their dance is unrehearsed
They warm and excite us 'cause we have the
brightest love

Two lights that shine as one
Morning glory and the midnight sun
Time we've learned to sail above
Time won't change the meaning of one love
ageless and ever evergreen

Standing beside her at the microphone, John Norman listened with his heart to overflowing. God, how he loved this woman! She was everything he had ceased to dream of long ago, when he'd decided that a woman couldn't exist for him on every level of need. But here she was—beautiful, warm, tender, giving, passionate, sensible, and independent. She was complete, he thought; she was complete without him. What could he offer her? Musical help? She'd make it eventually, without him, make it to the top. He was only helping to speed things up a little. Yet, she loved him. She really did seem to love him. He was grateful, yet terrified. Suppose some day she stopped loving him and went away? What would happen to him then?

I'm complete, thought Esther. Now that I have John Norman, I'm complete. I have everything in the world I want. My man and my music. And both are good, so very good. And getting better. God, I'm lucky. Thank you, God. Please don't let John Norman stop loving me.

John Norman's hand stole over hers, their fingers intertwining. Softly, he began to croon the song along with her, his rich, strong voice making a harmonious counterpoint to hers. Smiling at him, Esther tried to push his hand away; it was distracting her. But John Norman only clasped her fingers more tightly. Then he began to stroke her arm, reaching up her shoulder and caressing the nape of her neck where her hair was pinned up. Wriggling and shaking her head at him, Esther tried to move away. But it was impossible; she had to keep her station at the microphone, and she couldn't miss a beat. And John Norman knew it. He grinned at her wickedly as he continued to caress her.

Closing her eyes, Esther surrendered to his loving hands. And a strange thing happened. Her voice took on a new depth, a new huskiness. The lyrics of the song seemed even clearer and dearer to her now. As she glided from line to line, she began to touch her lover's face, his beard, his eyes, responding to his affection with affection of her own. Their voices blended . . .

"Chow chow," Ritchie's voice squawked from the control booth, breaking the mood.

"It's good," John Norman assured her, kissing her temple, but Esther shook her head, still uncertain of how to put her feelings about the music into words.

In the main recording room, a feast of Chinese food was being laid out by a pair of waiters from the takeout place down the street. Dallas, Pete, and Nicky had taken a break and were filling their paper plates high.

"Cookin', Esther, cookin' . . ." Lee called to her, waving a chopstick.

"Yeah," she replied.

"We'll cut it after we eat," said John Norman.

"Cut it?" asked Esther doubtfully. "So soon?"

"What's the matter?" John Norman wanted to know.

"I'm tired," Esther said evasively. "I've got a headache. I want an aspirin."

John Norman shook his head. "No aspirin," he decided. "You get ulcers, you bleed, you go into terminal acidosis, and you die. Eat your noodles," he ordered.

Esther wrinkled up her nose. "I don't like them," she complained.

"They're great. What do you mean, you don't like them?"

"They're hard." She sounded like a little girl, an unhappy little girl.

"Sure they're hard," grinned John Norman. "You said you liked noodles."

"Soft noodles, not hard noodles." She stuck her lower lip out.

John Norman knew that Esther and he weren't talking about noodles or Chinese food. He knew that she was scared, unwilling for some reason to actually cut the album today. He also knew that she'd come out with the reason if he gave her a few minutes. She always did. That was one of her most important character traits, he thought. She always called things as she saw them, no matter how the truth hurt.

"Don't eat the noodles, eat the chow mein," he said, gently putting a pair of chopsticks into her hand.

Esther poked at her plate of chow mein without interest. "Mmm," she said. She looked distracted, unhappy.

"What's the matter with it?" demanded John Norman.

"I didn't order the chow mein." Her voice was loud, her words rapid and resentful. "I ordered the moo goo gai pan, and I don't like the way I sang that song."

"Jesus, Esther, for an unaffiliated artiste, you are goddamn picky about your food! You said you liked the song."

Esther took a deep breath, then faced John Norman squarely, her blue eyes searching for his. "I lied. I like you. I don't like the song in F sharp. I could sing better in E flat. I don't like the kind of noodles you want me to eat." Her face was troubled, and she nibbled on her lip nervously.

"Eat what you want. Sing it any way you want. It's your song." John Norman kept his voice mild, his eyes on his plate.

"I want to sing it faster," said Esther stubbornly.

"Sing it faster. Eat."

"I don't want to eat before I sing," said Esther, putting her plate down. She was obviously near to tears, but she was fighting them back.

"You want to get married?" John Norman took a large bite of chow mein. His tone was light; he was half kidding her.

Esther felt a sudden rush of emotion take hold of her. She struggled to keep her cool. "Hell, no," she said with a saucy shake of her curly head. "You're totally undependable. You're irresponsible. You drink too much." She managed a shaky laugh.

John Norman looked up from his plate and spoke very slowly. "What if I quit the booze and became dependable. . . ?"

"Would you do that?" Esther's voice was quiet. She was suddenly very serious.

"Shit, no!" John Norman grinned. Fear, and the expression on Esther's face, had made him retreat. "Ritchie?" he called to the control booth.

Ritchie looked up from behind the glass. "Call 'em back," John Norman ordered. "I'll pay the meal penalty, and we'll just go into gold."

Ritchie shrugged and went off to summon the musicians back to record "Evergreen." This time, they would play it in Esther's tempo.

"Is it good?" asked Esther wearily, after they had listened to the playback. She was so exhausted, so drained physically and emotionally, that she could no longer tell good from bad. This was the first time she had ever heard her own music performed and recorded professionally, and it bewildered and disoriented her.

"Not bad," said John Norman laconically. But he was smiling.

"I'm tired," said Esther. She felt a hundred years old.

"Four down and six to go," said John Norman encouragingly.

Esther managed to smile at him, a small tremble of the lips. Her large blue eyes were filled with wonder. "I never heard it outside my head before," she marveled. "It sounds so . . . big."

Catching up her hand, John Norman kissed her fingertips one by one. There was nobody in the world like her, he thought. Nobody.

Chapter VII

The Los Angeles Forum was filled to overflowing with jubilant fans. The American Indian Relief Benefit Concert was a smashing success so far. Some of the top rock groups and stars in the country had appeared: The Allman Band, Maria Muldaur, America, Rita Coolidge, Paul Williams. During the Loggins & Messina set, Leon Russell strolled out unannounced to jam with them. Cher Bono did the same during the Allmans' set, then made a little speech about the plight of the American Indian. Other luminaries appeared. Marlon Brando, accompanied by Sacheen Little Feather, spoke eloquently and movingly. He got a standing ovation. So did Senator George McGovern. For most of the crowd, seeing him again was like old times. Shirley MacLaine and her brother Warren Beatty both put in an appearance, as did Jane Fonda and her husband, Tom Hayden. Vine DeLoria of the American Indian Movement and Russell Banks of Wounded Knee both made strong pleas for support. Chief Dan George was a majestic, commanding presence, excoriating the liberal crowd for ignoring the Indian while fighting for other minorities. They loved it. The star-studded show was the social and musical event of the year in L.A., but it was also like a great big, happy party. The crowd

Barbra Streisand lights up
the screen as Esther Hoffman in
"A Star is Born."

A musical moment in
"A Star is Born."

Esther and her backup girls,
The Oreos, playing a local
nightclub.

John Norman Howard acknowledging his audience.

Esther to John Norman:
"You're blowin' my act."

In trouble again; John Norman breaks up the Old Place.

John Norman had never met a girl like Esther before.

Booze for breakfast?
Esther prefers coffee.

John Norman Howard and his fans.

He's hurt! John Norman's hurt, and they won't let Esther near him.

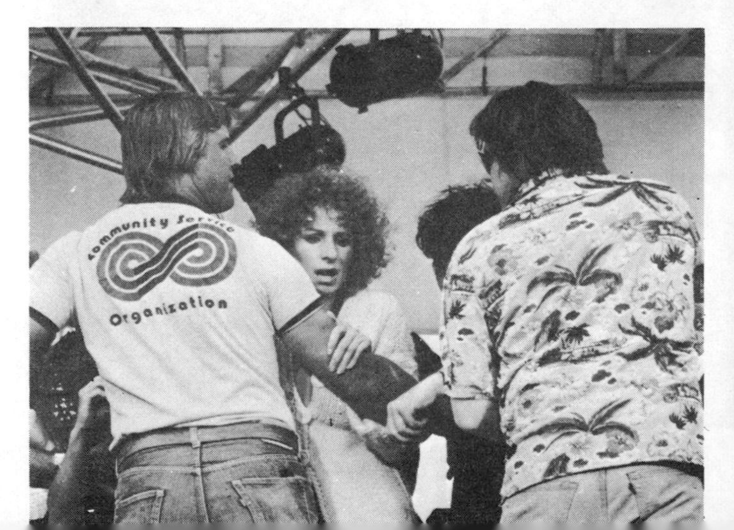

That disc jockey is going to get his case of booze in a way he won't forget.

The Indian benefit concert that starts Esther Hoffman on her way to stardom.

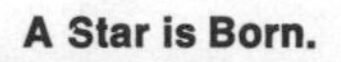

A Star is Born.

When you're hot, everybody wants to get in on the act.

John Norman and Esther—for better, for worse, man and wife.

A rare moment of complete serenity for John Norman and Esther.

If we could only stay like this!

A house isn't home until you've built it with your own hands.

Love among the wedding presents.

Esther with Tony Orlando and Rita Coolidge at the Grammy Awards.

"Fight me, you bastard!" Esther battles to save her marriage.

**After the rage come
the tears and the loving.**

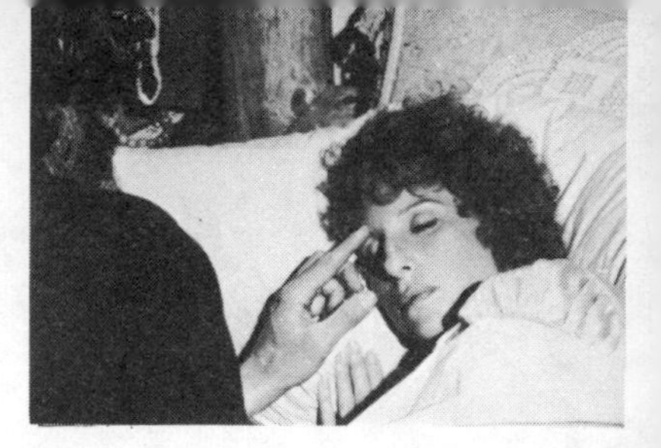

"Goodbye, my dearest love."

Esther kneels by John Norman's body.

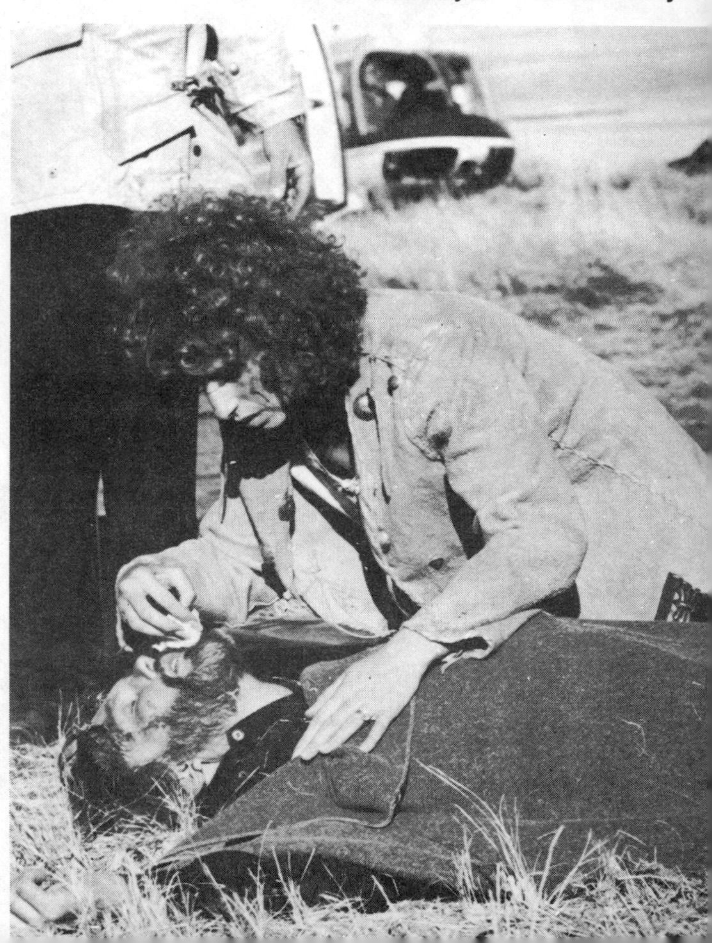

Esther sits alone after John Norman's death.

"I'm Esther Hoffman Howard."

Barbra Steisand sings her heart out and thousands cheer.

Kris Kristofferson as John Norman Howard in "A Star is Born."

and the performers were filled with the kind of warm comradeship that had been missing since the days of civil rights, Vietnam, and the McGovern campaign. It was as if—for one night—"the Movement" had been born all over again.

The John Norman Howard Speedway was also on the bill, and though the crowd couldn't have been in a friendlier mood, many among them wondered what would go wrong this time. By now, they had all heard about the smashup at the big outdoor concert and about the cancelled tour. They had read the stinging account in *Rolling Stone*, with its screaming headline, "HAS COCAINE FRIED HIS BRAIN?" The article ended:

> John Norman Howard has been a major star on the rock scene for several years now. His large following has bought his records, sold out his concerts—made him a rich and powerful man.
>
> And once upon a time, he deserved it. Once upon a time, he was an original, innovative musical talent. But if last week's drugged-up idiocy is any indication, he's not just slipping, he's dive-bombing. We think he owes the rock and roll public more than he's giving. We say John Norman Howard is making a mockery of rock and roll. We say to him, if you can't do better than this, man, go away. Just go away.

And he had sort of gone away. No new album had been released (the record company had breathed hard all over Brian Wexler about this; they didn't give a fuck *how* hot John Norman thought this Esther Hoffman was, their contract was with the Speedway), and tonight would be the Speedway's first public appearance since the aborted tour.

Backstage, Bobby Ritchie and Brian Wexler were

closeted together in a tiny dressing room. Bobby sat on an old desk, methodically striking one match after another, blowing it out, and tossing it across the room in the direction of a wastebasket. The floor was littered with the burnt stubs. Brian paced back and forth, his head bowed, pulling at his lower lip.

"You thinkin' what I'm thinkin'?" he asked, not stopping, not looking up.

"What?" Bobby said. He blew out another match.

"That he's even more fucked-up than usual tonight?"

"Hard to tell," Bobby said. He put down the matches and gazed up at the ceiling, his head cocked to one side. "He's pretty goddamn drunk, I'll tell you that," he said. "And you know our star. He probably did a couple of reds for breakfast along with the usual sauce. Then he probably started hittin' the coke in a serious way along about four o'clock. But I stopped trackin' his intake years ago, Brian. It's a full-time job."

"Okay, okay, cut the sarcasm, Bobby," Brian said.

Things had been strained between them lately. Brian knew Bobby was royally pissed about all the time "wasted" on Esther's album. He knew, in fact, that nobody in the band was happy about not working on their own stuff. At one point, Lee Dallas had even come to him to complain. "The Speedway's a good band, man," he had said, "and we don't need her. I'm wonderin' if we even need *him*." But Brian argued that what Esther's album was doing for John Norman was worth the time and energy. Sure, her sound wasn't the band's sound, but wasn't John Norman healthier than he had been in years? Wasn't he working harder and better than any of them could remember? The work with Esther would be over soon, he assured them. Then John Norman would be ready to get back to his own stuff, and it would be better than ever.

It hadn't quite worked out that way. A week ago,

when they pulled off the album to go into rehearsals for the benefit, John Norman had gone straight back to the old pattern: Heavy drugs, lateness, sloppy playing, egomania, temper. Brian freaked. He had worked his ass off to get them on the bill, and it had been uphill all the way. When he first called the promoter who was organizing the show—Jackie Epstein—to "volunteer" the services of the John Norman Howard Speedway, the reaction was what he had expected.

"You gotta be kiddin'," Epstein had said. "Listen, Brian, we've known each other a while. You know this is a benefit gig. I'm givin' my time, just like everybody else. It's a big show and a lot of work. The last thing I need is that screwed-up star of yours. You may not have noticed, but around the business, your boy's name spells shit. Thanks, baby, but no thanks."

Brian had persisted. The Speedway made a substantial "contribution" to the Indian cause. A meeting was set up between Jackie Epstein and John Norman Howard, during which the star remained impressively straight. Brian phoned Epstein every day—even put other people up to calling—urging him to put John Norman on the bill.

Finally, Epstein relented. Okay, the Speedway would go on, but late in the show, and not as a featured act. Brian swore on his mother's grave that he'd have his star there on time and straight. Well, he was on time, but John Norman was not exactly what you'd call straight.

Brian paced some more. Bobby went back to his match routine. The door opened a crack and Jackie Epstein stuck his head in.

"Your boy's up next," he said curtly. "Fifteen minutes."

"Right," Brian said. The door closed. Brian looked at Bobby.

"Don't sweat it, Brian," Bobby said wearily, "I'll

get him on stage. I always do." Brian suddenly exploded, all of the tension of the last months coming together in one angry outburst.

"It's not *getting* him on stage that worries me, you self-satisfied motherfucker," he shouted. "It's what he might do *after* he gets there! Do you realize that this isn't exactly your average rock concert, that the press here could absolutely destroy us—I mean finish us for good?" He began pacing furiously again, almost talking to himself. "I mean, it's not just your regular rock press. This is a *political* event. *Time* is here, and *Newsweek*. Fuckin' *Women's Wear Daily*." He crossed the room again in three steps. "All three networks. The New York *Times*. You name it, it's here." He stopped and turned to Bobby, who sat picking his teeth with the matchbook. "You know, Bobby," he said coldly, "the trouble with you is you just don't give a shit anymore." Bobby Ritchie shrugged and slid his body off the desk.

"Let's go get the man together," he said. Epstein was waiting for them in the hall. The three of them made their way through the crush of reporters, photographers, cameramen, and others to John Norman's dressing room. None of them was happy with what they found there.

At least his outfit was together—a simple, well-cut, Western-style black suit, black boots, dark patterned shirt open to the waist, the silver concho belt. But it was clear to them all that *he* wasn't together. He sat sprawled on an old couch, his head thrown back, his legs spread apart, and cradling a half-empty quart bottle of vodka. His eyes were closed, and he did not move when they came in.

"Okay, sweetheart, it's showtime," Bobby said, pulling a plastic Baggie of coke from the pocket of his jeans.

"Jesus-fucking-Christ!" Epstein exploded. "You think you're gonna get this basket case on *stage*? Man, he is a *mess*!" He turned to Brian angrily. "I warned you, you son of a bitch," he said, shaking his finger in Brian's face. John Norman swung his head around and looked up. His eyes rolled; he smiled and giggled.

"Now, you be cool, man," he slurred. "Everythin' gonna be okay. John Norman Howard gonna knock 'em dead."

"Here, baby, somethin' for your nose," Bobby said, offering the uncut coke from the end of his finger. John Norman took several long snorts. It seemed enough to energize him. He got up, swaying a little.

"Everythin' gonna be fine as wine," he said. The promoter looked him up and down. Bombed out of his mind and nothin' but trouble, he thought. He thought back to Janis Joplin as she was toward the end. He looked from Brian to Bobby and back.

"You guys are un-fucking-believable," he said, shaking his head from side to side. "Just un-fucking-believable." He turned and stomped out of the dressing room.

"Whassamatter with that shithead?" John Norman said. He upended the bottle of vodka, chugalugging the booze in big gulps. Bobby took the bottle away and grabbed him by one arm. Brian grabbed the other.

"Come on, baby, let's go," he said. They guided him through the doorway and began to push their way through the crowded hallway toward the stage.

"More snow," John Norman said. He could hardly stand. Bobby pulled the Baggie from his pocket and simply opened it under John Norman's nose. John Norman inhaled deeply. So he O.D.'s on stage, Bobby thought, so what? With a heavy, slow hand John Norman wiped the flecks of coke off his beard, then licked his fingers.

"Where's Esther?" he mumbled. "Wanna see Esther."

Bobby looked for her in the crush of groupies, roadies, and press. He spotted her finally, standing against the wall by herself, calmly observing the noisy scene. She was dressed in a stylish three-piece suit, cut like a man's, and a striped shirt open at the neck. That was another thing that bugged Ritchie about her. The others—the chicks before—had always dressed like the trash they were. Not her. That fuckin' broad, he thought. That Esther. She's gotta go if we're gonna salvage this act. She's got too much power, too much control. Bobby had always controlled John Norman's women before, knew just when to buy them off, threaten them—whatever it took to get rid of them. The women were like the drugs as far as he was concerned. He, Ritchie, had to control both in order to control his star. But not this one. She wouldn't budge. She was there to stay.

She saw them picking their way down the long hallway and began to make her way toward them. My God, she thought, he looks terrible. She had been worried sick all week. It had all been going so well between them. They were working hard and playing hard. He was devoted to her and to her career. Her album seemed to mean everything to him, and he made that forcefully clear to everyone. Yet as soon as he went back to the band, he started to fall apart again, and even she couldn't get to him. Why? What had happened? He had been particularly weird today: secretive, preoccupied, staring at her for long moments and then laughing softly to himself. He was behaving like a little boy up to no good, and because she knew as well as anyone how important tonight's appearance was to his faltering career, she was worried. "Johnny," she had asked in the car on the way down, "what's the matter?" He had feigned surprise. Nothing, he said, nothing at all. She smelled trouble. She couldn't tell exactly how smashed he was. His driving had been okay. Over the months they had been together, she had learned to her surprise that he occasionally pretended to be more stoned than he really was, depending on who was around and what suited his purpose.

Ah, booze, he thought as he allowed himself to be led staggering toward the stage. Good ol' juice. Ya' can't beat it with a stick. These here other drugs of the twentieth century certainly are fine, God knows, but do give me my al-ko-hall! When you've drunk just the right amount, when you hit that certain stoned point, there ain't no high like it in the world. Yessiree, like my granddaddy always said, never trust a man who don't drink. He laughed out loud, looking from Bobby to Brian. They were silent and grim-faced. They think I can't pull it off any more, he thought. They think I'm so fucked up I can't even *stand* up. Well, you just watch this good ol' boy. 'Cause what he got planned for tonight gonna make you shit your *pants*!

Esther made her way through the crowd to his side. Brian made room for her as she put one arm around John Norman's waist and slung his arm over her shoulder. He looked down at her with a wobbly grin.

"How you doin', honey?" he said. "You ready for tonight?"

"It's not me we're worried about," she said. "Are *you* ready?"

"Oh, I'm ready," he drawled, laughing to himself again, "am ready, ready, Teddy."

Slowly, they plodded up the ramp to the stage entrance. The guys were there, along with Freddy, Danzinger, Epstein, and a couple of roadies. Everybody looked worried. A roadie strapped on the big Gibson. John Norman demanded one more hit of coke. Bobby obliged. As he clumsily tried to give Esther a kiss, a booming voice announced the Speedway, and Bobby hustled him out on to the stage. They took up their positions in front of the spotlit backdrop—a huge blowup of a classic painting, the noble head of a great Sioux warrior—and were greeted by warm, if subdued, applause. They tuned their instruments. The crowd grew quiet, waiting. John Norman stood center stage, swaying slightly, his head bowed. He picked at his guitar. He blew into his mike loudly a few times. The band waited for him to start. Nothing. John Norman giggled into the mike. The clutch of people at the side of the stage watched tensely. Don't blow it, Johnny, Esther thought. Please don't blow this one.

Finally, Lee Dallas counted down, and the band started the opening number. John Norman stood staring out at the audience. It was obvious after the first few bars that he wasn't with them. Lee signaled the others and they stopped playing. Silence. A low murmur passed through the packed hall. Seconds went by. At the side of the stage, Brian ground his teeth until his jaw ached.

"Oh, dear," Freddy murmured.

Epstein cracked, "Straight and on time, eh?"

Esther stood a little to the front of the others, not moving. She stared straight at John Norman and sent out her strongest good vibes.

John Norman blew loudly into the mike again. "Dum da dumm dum dum," he mumbled into it.

The crowd was chattering noisily now. They had half expected this. In a way, they half wanted it. John Norman suddenly struck the opening chords of the number. The band, caught off guard, quickly tried to pick it up, but it was all ragged and out of synch. John Norman stopped playing as abruptly as he had begun, and the tune died. He laughed.

The crowd began back-talking him. "Come on, man!" somebody shouted. "Get him off!" demanded another voice. There were scattered boos and whistles. He was spoiling their beautiful evening. It had been a glorious coming together, and now this washed-up drunk was trying to ruin it all. The knot of people just offstage stood frozen in a tableau.

"I don't fucking believe it," Brian hissed through clenched teeth. "He just can't do this again. He just can't!"

"He's doin' it," Bobby said quietly. John Norman squinted out at the restless crowd through the blinding lights.

"Hey, hey, I'm sorry," he said into his mike. They weren't interested in his apologies. There were more and louder catcalls. One section began stomping rhythmically. Others took it up.

"Wait just a second. Y'all wait a second," he said. They quieted a little. "I just decided y'all didn't need to hear any o' that same old shit." There were loud boos.

"Shit is right," somebody yelled.

"You've had it, man," came from another.

"Hold it!" John Norman yelled over the noise. "All right, now, which one of us do you think is smarter, you or me?" His speech was slurred, and they greeted it with a loud chorus of boos and whistles.

"Listen, listen to me!" he demanded. "I wanna tell you somethin'. Since this is such a good benefit for such a good cause, we figure—even if you don't—that you might deserve somethin' better than you're gettin', okay?"

They didn't like it at all. Their protests grew louder, and it was clear they were really angry now. But John Norman went on, raising his voice to match their noise. "So we're gonna do you a favor whether you deserve it or not," he yelled into the mike. "Me and the boys just run into somethin' that was pretty weird and pretty real. And it's so pretty that it's frightenin'." But they were in an uproar.

"Give us the same old shit, man!" somebody shouted, and others picked it up. Soon they were in full chant, clapping and stomping.

"Same old shit!"

"Same old shit!"

"Same old shit!"

"Hey, hey!" he yelled. He waited and they grew a little quieter. "If ya' think ya' got a corner on the ignorant market, ya' haven't." His voice was full of contempt and they knew it. People were standing and booing him now. Others wadded up their programs and threw them at the stage.

"Shut up!" he shouted. "Do yourself a favor and listen to somethin' good, all right?"

"No! No!" they shouted back. But he stood his ground, not moving from his mike, but not playing, either. The guys in the band didn't know what to do.

"Okay, Bobby," Jackie Epstein said, "That's it. Yank him."

Bobby looked at the promoter. "You yank him, baby. I ain't goin' out on that stage."

Esther stood watching John Norman, her stomach a knot of pain. She didn't know what to do. Should *she* call to him to get off? What was he thinking, for God's sake? Was he waiting for them to storm the stage and kill him?

The crowd grew bored with their own protests. As they quieted down a little, John Norman slowly took off his guitar and walked toward the side of the stage. The spotlight followed him as he weaved and stumbled up to Esther, smiling broadly. He reached for her hand and she pulled back. He laughed and made another grab for her. Brian and Gary tried to pull him off her, while Freddy moved to protect her. They all reacted as if he had simply, finally, lost his mind.

"Come on, honey, come on," he said gently. He had hold of her now and wouldn't let go.

"Get back on that fucking stage!" Brian said.

"Darling, darling, *please*," Esther pleaded. But John Norman had her by both hands now and was dragging her toward the stage. She pulled one hand free and slapped him hard across the face.

"What are you doing, you bastard!" she yelled, but he just laughed at her.

"You're gonna do fantastic," he said. Suddenly

ripping the backstage sticker pass off her lapel, he began to pull her toward center stage again. She struggled, but Brian grabbed her by both shoulders from behind and squeezed hard.

"For God's sake, do something, even if it's *wrong*!" he hissed. Esther stopped resisting and stood looking at John Norman for a minute. Then she allowed him to lead her by the hand out onto the huge stage.

"He planned it, you know," Bobby said thoughtfully to Brian. "The son of a bitch set us all up. It's fucking sabotage, and he meant it."

"This here's a friend o' mine, Esther Hoffman," John Norman said into his mike. There was scattered applause. Not that they recognized the name or the girl. She looked as if she was standing in front of a firing squad. But they'd applaud anything if it meant they'd get rid of him.

John Norman let go of Esther's hand. "Woman in the Moon," he said to her softly, turning to the band and repeating the song title. With that, he loped off stage.

She took the mike from its stand and turned to look at the guys. They stared back at her. They had backed up the tune on dozens of takes for the album, but they knew she had never done it live, she'd never even stood before an audience this size before.

Yes, she *was* nervous. But she was confident, too. Confident in her voice and in her music. Maybe she didn't plan this, but that didn't mean she couldn't pull it off, goddamn it.

"Okay, fellas," Esther said, and counted down into the song.

It was a beautiful, soft ballad, sexy and sad. As she slowly got into it, the audience hushed. She felt their response, felt the skepticism and anger melting away. Her voice grew strong and assured. It soared. She began to move about the stage, expertly snaking the mike cord, playing to them as if she'd done it a thousand times. And she had, in her head. She had always known that someday she'd stand in front of this audience. She felt fabulous, and she sounded fabulous.

I was warned as a child of thirteen
Not to act too strong
Try to look like you belong but don't push girl
Save your time and trouble
Don't misbehave

I was raised in a "no you don't world"
Overrun with rules
Memorize your lines and move as directed
That's an age old story
Everybody knows that's a worn out song

But you and I are changing that tune
We're learning new rhythms from the woman
I said the woman in the moon
Little sister, little brother
Keep on pushin'
Don't believe a word about
Things you heard about
Askin' too much too soon
'Cause they can hold back the tide
But they can never hold the woman in the moon

I believe there's a best of both worlds
Mixing old and new
Recognizing change is seldom expected
As I long suspected
They believed that strange was a word for wrong

Well not in my song
'Cause you, you and I are changing that tune
We're learning new rhythms from that woman in
the moon
Little sister, little brother
Keep on pushin'
Don't believe a word about
Things you heard about

Askin' too much too soon
'Cause they can hold back the tide
But they can never hold the woman
I said the woman in the moon

John Norman watched from offstage, beaming at Esther, proud and happy. Bobby stood next to him, shaking with rage.

"Goddamn you, John Norman, you set this whole thing up. You didn't tell me, you didn't tell the band, you didn't tell a fuckin' soul. Maybe you think this is cute, but let me tell you somethin'. You don't fuck your own band ever—not for anybody. You gave up *our* gig and made it *hers*. If you think you're gonna get away with that, you're fuckin' crazier than I thought." John Norman didn't take his eyes off Esther.

"Shut up, Bobby, and go backstage and get the girls," he said.

"What girls, man?"

"Her backup, asshole. Phyllis and Sydelle. I got 'em waitin' backstage."

"John Norman, I'm warnin' you. . . ." Bobby began.

"Fuck you, Bobby. Do what I tell you," John Norman cut him off

Bobby stood for a moment, clenching and unclenching his fists. Never before had he wanted so much to beat the shit out of the guy. He turned and stalked off.

John Norman ignored him and his anger. All he could think of was Esther out there, doing it, making it, as he always knew she could. I did it! he thought. They love her! He relished the sense of power the audience response gave him.

As Esther finished the song, the applause was tumultuous. She stood center stage, breathless, her face flushed, taking it all in. Though she was a little stunned, she was also triumphant. She had always known she could handle them, that she had the talent and power to control an audience. Now she had proved it. And it felt damn good.

Esther took one low bow, replaced the mike on its stand, and rushed off stage. John Norman stood waiting for her. He had snatched a single rose from a groupie and now presented it to Esther. As the applause continued, they stood smiling at each other. She had completely forgotten she was ever mad at him.

"I love you," she said.

"Go on back," he said, "I'll be right here."

Esther hardly needed the direction. She rushed back on to take command of what was clearly *her* stage. A gleeful Phyllis and Sydelle followed her, and as Esther cued the band, they launched into a rousing number called "I Believe in Love."

Thinking like a pro already, Esther knew that after the ballad, this was just the song to get the fans up and on their feet. While the girls executed a slick little step they had worked up, Esther belted out the number, pacing back and forth, whipping the mike cord behind her, gesturing, breaking into a boogie at just the right moment, throwing her head back for the big notes, working the band to a frenzy. She played the astonished audience for all they were worth. She got *down*. Except for the fact that they had never heard or seen her before, the crowd could never have guessed that this lady was not a seasoned veteran. A star was being born, and they were watching it happen.

I see
Faces . . . covered-up and empty-eyed,
Empty spaces . . . where there used to be a soul
  inside.
Nothing and no one ever gets to you,
Seems the wind could blow right through you,

Believing in gods that never knew you.
I believe in love.

I believe in love.
I believe in feeling good
And that's feeling love.

Now, worry . . . climbing up your money tree,
You go to hurry . . . monkey do what monkey see.
You're on a one-way street and you're speeding,
Missing the signs you oughta be reading,
Passing things you'll later be needing.
I believe in love

I believe it—nobody sold me
Always knew it—nobody told me
I believe in someone to hold me
I believe in love

I believe in love. I do
I believe in feeling good
And that's feeling love!

The number ended, and a gigantic wave of applause broke over the stage. The audience was on its feet, stomping, cheering, whistling, shouting for more. Back and forth Esther and the girls went, taking bow after bow. John Norman clapped 'till his hands ached, smiled 'till it hurt. He was bursting with pride and love.

When Esther finally left the stage, she ran smack into a small riot. Flashbulbs popped in her face, blinding her. TV minicams were rolling; from all sides, reporters shouted questions at her. Brian and Gary grabbed her roughly to protect her and guide her through the crush. John Norman moved to the background, smiling proudly.

Bobby led the way, cutting a path for her toward the exit ramp. The rolling ocean of faceless reporters moved right along with them, clamoring for her attention. Everybody was semi-hysterical, caught up in that rare moment they all shared—the discovery of a star. No matter what happens, Brian thought, John Norman Howard, that cold-blooded, scheming egomaniac, always pulls the fat out of the fire. I wonder if he understands that this time he forgot to save his *own* ass?

"Of course she's going to happen," Gary Danzinger shouted to a frantic reporter. "I'll have a bio for you tomorrow."

"She's already happened, you saw her happen," Brian announced triumphantly.

They were both ad-libbing their tails off, trying to give the impression that the discovery was *their* coup, a carefully planned surprise designed to knock the music establishment on its ass. After all, wasn't that what they were supposed to be famous for?

"I think she's from Maryland, Florida, someplace like that," Gary jived a guy from *People*.

"We'll be releasing a single right away," Brian assured the girl from *Womens' Wear Daily*.

Esther was almost lost in the crush, but she stayed cool, handling it all as if she'd been through it before. She scanned the crowd for John Norman, spotting him at last at the fringes. Beaming at her, he winked. She smiled and winked back. She signaled: Come, share this with me. He signaled back: Enjoy; it's yours, and we'll have each other later. She turned back to the noisy gang of press people, feeling good and warm and close to him. She knew it would be like this. He knew, too, she thought. He had made it happen for her. Esther had no way of knowing the price he would have to pay for it.

Freddy Lowenstein stood waiting at the foot of the ramp—Ever-Ready Freddy, who now grabbed Esther and kissed her on both cheeks, acting as if they had always been sisters.

"Es! Darling! What can I say?" she cooed, locking

an arm around Esther's waist in a proprietary way.

This bitch is incredible, Esther thought. What's with this "Es" routine? Nobody had ever called her that before. Reporters and photographers pressed closer, demanding more pictures, interviews, information. Who was this fantastic new singer?

"You think she's as terrific as we do? I'm gonna give you a chance to air-test her," Gary babbled to a skinny little D.J. "Esther, say hi to Ricky Wingo, KCET-Seattle."

Freddy was whispering rapidly into Esther's ear, not about to loosen her hold. "We could do it one of two ways, Es," she said. "The advantage of a personal-service contract is that, as your lawyers will confirm. . ."

"Actually, I have no lawyers," Esther cut in, flippantly, putting Freddy down.

Funny, she thought. This isn't hard, or scary at all. I can handle this.

A short, middle-aged man right out of the 1950s—grizzled crew cut, rimless glasses, bow tie, drip-dry white shirt, baggy suit—shoved his way to her side. His press pass showed he was a wire-service man, the type who neither knows nor cares about pop music, but always lands the assignment.

"Esther . . . *Hoffman*?" he said, his tone querulous. "What name are you performing under?"

"Thank you, yes, thank you," Esther said to an adoring fan. "I'm sorry, what did you say?" she asked the little man. Then, turning to Ricky Wingo, "Hello, Mr. Wingo."

The crowd continued to swirl around her, and she smiled warmly, politely acknowledging the many compliments. She looked and acted like a star. She felt like one, too. "I'm sorry, what did you say?" she asked, turning her attention to the wire-service man.

"You ever think of changing your name?" the reporter asked.

"Yes. But I don't want to," she said.

"Esther *Hoffman*? It sounds like . . ."

"But we should talk about a personal-service contract," Freddy butted in. Esther ignored her.

"Why should I change it?" she retorted. "It's who I am. Besides, I'd have to change my social security, my driver's license, get new stationery—it would be a bother."

"It sounds so . . . religious," the reporter said, scratching his head.

"Es, Es!," Freddy pleaded, "your lawyers will confirm, a personal-service contract . . ." God! she thought, stars! They're all alike. They want it so bad, they'll kill for it. But when they get it, they start behaving like children. If you didn't lock them into a deal early, they just let their business affairs turn into an absolute mess!

Freddy felt a hand grip her arm and, turning, saw it was John Norman.

"Let me tell you there are no advantages to a personal-service contract," he said to Esther as he pried Freddy loose. Esther let John Norman steer her rapidly toward the door, but shot a quizzical look over her shoulder at the wire-service reporter. "Are you anti-Semitic?" she said.

She turned to John Norman as he hustled her out of the door, reporters still in hot pursuit. "How'd you know what she was talkin' about?"

"I played this gig before," he said.

They were suddenly outside in the relative quiet of the street. She stopped in her tracks and looked around.

"What just happened?" she said in mock surprise. Then they both cracked up, laughing like a pair of maniacs as they dove into his Ferrari. He had set that up, too. Knowing they would need a getaway car, he had instructed one of his roadies to have it ready, the motor running. He threw it into first and roared down the alley just as the pursuing reporters made it to the door. When he stopped at the corner to make the turn into traffic, she threw her arms around him and hugged him wildly. He gave her a great big kiss.

"You did it! You did it!" he shouted at the top of his lungs, thumping the steering wheel with his fist. "It's all yours, Esther. Everything you want. Your personal piece of the American dream!" He eased the car into traffic.

"It's not *everything* I want," she said. "You know what I really want?" She was subdued now, and her tone was very serious.

"I want you to know what it *means*," he said, ignoring her question. He literally squirmed in his seat with excitement, high on her success and obsessed with his star-maker role. It was the first good thing he'd done for anybody in years, and he had forgotten how satisfying that could be. He talked wildly.

"On the road . . . every cliché you ever heard is true . . . you got your fluorescent tan, junk food, and noisy maids . . . an endless boogie from motel to motel . . ."

"I want to marry you," Esther said calmly. Either he didn't hear her or didn't want to.

"You got your basic meeting with your basic mayor," he rattled on, "your keys to the city—except you don't know what city you're in . . ."

"I want to marry you," she repeated slowly. She looked cool and matter-of-fact, but her insides were churning. She could feel her heart pounding away.

John Norman stopped the car in the middle of the street and stared straight ahead in silence. She had gotten through. He rested his long arms on the steering wheel and buried his face in them for a moment. He looked up at her.

"No, you don't. I drink too much, I throw my money away . . ." He paused. She looked squarely at him, her face expressionless. "I owe the government a hundred and eighty grand," he said.

"Don't you want to?" she asked.

"That's not the point."

"So do I," she said, as if it were settled. "We'll do it together. You'd be lucky to have me."

A chorus of honking horns blared at them from behind. John Norman had stopped the car so as to block two lanes of traffic. He turned in his seat and shouted back. "Shut up! We're talkin' here!"

He shook his fist at the irate drivers. Anything to take his attention away from her. He was trying to play cool, too. They had had this conversation once before, he remembered. He had popped the question as a joke, but she had turned serious and it scared the shit out of him. Now *she* was doing the asking, and it was no joke. It freaked him. He wanted to . . . but, no, how could it ever work, what if he hurt her, too . . .

"Don't bullshit me, Esther! I might start believing you!" He sounded mad, and he was looking at her angrily. She smiled at him. She knew he wanted it, but she also knew that deep down inside he was just a scared kid, always running away. She took his frowning face in both her hands.

"John Norman Howard, I love you," she said. The horns honked on and on.

Chapter VIII

They were married in the courtyard of the old City Hall in Phoenix, Arizona. They had fallen in love with the grace of the ancient, Spanish-style building, with its glazed tiles and Mediterranean arches. Both of them wore white, because this wedding, not the first for either of them, was actually the first wedding in the history of the world. It was to be their beginning.

John Norman wore a white suit, a white shirt, and a white rose, pinned to his jacket. Even his boots were white. His eyes were very clear and blue; he had not touched drugs or booze in several days. Every time he looked at Esther, he broke into a smile and his heart filled with an abundance of feeling he knew he could never express. Jesus, he loved her! Everything was going to be different now that she was going to be his wife.

The small white veil over Esther's blond hair was showered with flower petals. Dressed in a short white gown of antique lace, she wore sheer white stockings and high heels. She was so nervous, so happy, that she felt the color rising up into her cheeks. My God, she thought, a blushing bride! Could you believe it? But she had faith, faith in John Norman, faith in herself, faith in their love. There would be problems;

there were *already* problems, but John Norman was changing. She could see the changes in him, and they warmed her.

"Awright," the clerk said. "Esther Leona Hoffman, you take this man as your husband?" The clerk was a Chicano woman; she'd grumbled when Esther had insisted that the ceremony be outdoors, but she'd given in at last, with good grace.

"That's it?" Esther looked up, astonished. "What about love, honor, and obey, and until death do us part, and all that?"

The two witnesses—John Norman had grabbed them off the street as they'd passed by—broke up at Esther's plaintive question.

"Honey, this is what they tell us to say," replied the clerk, somewhat dolefully. "You want the long form, you gotta do it in church."

"Anyway," John Norman reminded Esther, "obey is out. We say cherish. The dawn of a new century."

It is, thought Esther. It is the dawn of a new century. We're gonna live together a hundred years, and then a hundred more. We're gonna have dozens of hit records and a kid for every hit. We're gonna be rich and famous and loved. But they'll let us alone. They'll leave us with each other, to the peace and the privacy we need, and John Norman will grow strong, and he'll let me love him as I know he needs it. It *will* happen; I know it will. Please, God, she added, superstitious.

"I already stretched doin' this out here 'stead of my office," stated the clerk. "You gonna do it or not?"

"I'm gonna do it," said Esther with resolution.

"Me, too," John Norman said.

"Well, good, then. I pronounce you man and wife. Listen, we got this little sample gift they leave off to pass out." She handed them a cheaply wrapped gift box, the kind of thing that local Chambers of Commerce provide for newlyweds and new homeowners.

John Norman took Esther into his arms for the first kiss of their married life. As her arms wound around his neck, the clerk broke into a grin and the spectators into applause. Kissing the astonished clerk, the newlyweds jumped into the big Jeep CJ-7 and headed off for "home."

"Home" was a mystery to Esther; John Norman refused to tell her anything about where they were going. He was enjoying his puzzling stance, and the more Esther begged to know, the more enigmatic he became.

"How far is this place?" Esther kept asking.

"A ways." He would say no more.

They drove for hours, first on the freeway, then on a series of increasingly narrow two-lane blacktop roads. Arizona stretched flat on either side of the Jeep, the green farmland eventually giving way to reddish-brown ranch land and desert. Mesas shimmered in the distance; Esther had never seen country like this before.

To break the monotony, she unpacked the Chamber of Commerce gift box, pulling at the sleazy paper with her long fingernails. As she read out the list of items to John Norman, she choked so hard with laughter that she could hardly finish.

"Toothpaste, breakfast cereal fortified with B-12, gentle detergent for dainties . . ." She was unable to continue, and John Norman threw back his head and roared. ". . . decaffeinated instant coffee, pre-moistened Handi-Wipes . . ." The tears rolled down her cheeks. "Strawberry douche . . ." she beat off John Norman's outstretched hand, as he pantomimed grabbing it and drinking it. "Fabric softener, stain remover, eyeglass cleaning tissues, deodorant, and antihistamines for allergies. It's a perfect marriage kit!"

They stopped only when they had to, for gas and food. They ate in the car. Esther struggled to make sandwiches in her lap, sliding ingredients everywhere and giggling constantly.

"Yours is pastrami," she told John Norman as she handed over a fat sandwich.

"What's pastrami?" John Norman joked, swigging beer.

"I have to teach you everything?" she mocked.

Toward sunset, they turned onto a dirt road. After a few miles, that ended, and they went roaring along across the desert, the jeep raising a tail of dust behind them. The landscape was empty as far as the eye could see. The sunset was made to order: brilliant reds, oranges, and purples, straight out of a Hollywood Western. Esther drew in her breath, overwhelmed by its magnificence.

"How much farther is it?" she asked finally.

"We're on it," he said.

"This is your farm?" She was incredulous.

"Ranch, Esther. This is a ranch. This is your average, eighty-eight-thousand-acre non-working ranch."

"Jesus! You mean as far as I can see, you *own* it?"

"You and I own it, babe," he said, laughing.

He was always amazed at her naiveté, at how incredibly wide-eyed and innocent she was. So fresh, so clean. "Community property," he went on. "You, me, and the First National Bank of Tucson, and the Security Pacific in L.A., and the Banker's Trust in Phoenix . . . And oh, yeah, Brian's got a second mortgage tucked in there somewhere. Outright, you and I own maybe a quarter-acre."

At last, John Norman stopped at the crest of a low but wide plateau. The view was spectacular, the silence vast. Esther climbed slowly out of the jeep and looked around, stunned. He was grinning.

"It's like the ocean, the way it slopes away," she said. "Where's the ranchhouse?"

"You're standin' in it," he said matter-of-factly. "Right now, you're in the kitchen."

"Kitchen? But I thought you lived here?"

"Camped out," he said, "figurin' out where I'd sleep and where I'd watch the moon come up." She looked down and saw that the floor plan of the house had been staked out with pegs and strings.

"Why didn't you finish it?" she asked.

"Didn't have a reason to. It was just in my head."

They looked at each other for a moment in silence, then both smiled softly. They knew he had a reason now.

"What do ya think?" he said at last.

"Where's the bedroom?" she asked.

John Norman laughed and got out of the jeep, leading her to another square inside the string. As she was about to step into it, he picked her up and carried her over. He started to put her down, but before her feet touched the ground, he lifted her again.

"Lemme get a blanket. You're gonna get stickers all over your ass." She laughed and pulled him down with her, enveloping him.

"I don't care," she said.

"That's the spirit that won the West," John Norman said, and they both giggled.

They made love there, in their new "house." Very slowly and very tenderly, alone in the silent desert. When it was over, they lay exhausted in each other's arms, listening to the quiet.

They slept in the open under the stars. Esther swore she'd never seen a sky like it in her life. "Brooklyn it ain't," she said.

In the morning, they drove into the nearby ranching community for supplies, buying yards and yards of Indian rugs which they would stitch together with heavy cord to build a teepee—a temporary home while they built their own house with their own hands. John Norman spent money like a madman in the little town. He bought a huge, beat-up old D-8 caterpillar tractor with blade plows from one rancher, a '56 Ford flatbed truck from another; he ordered two motorcycles from an astonished farm machinery dealer—a 350 cc for Esther and a 650 for himself—and fifteen head of cattle from a local breeder. They practically bought out the dry goods store, and Esther fell in love with Western-style farm clothes and long, colorful cotton dresses. She bought a dozen straw hats for good measure. The hardware store they went through like a pair of guerrilla raiders, leaving with well over fifteen hundred dollars' worth of tools and equipment.

They ordered a windmill built at the local lumberyard, saying they'd be back for more soon. "Buildin' a house, ya know," John Norman told the owner.

The old town was suspicious of this pair of young kooks. Who the hell were they? Where'd they get all that money? Never seen anything like 'em, that lanky, bearded young fella and that strange-lookin' frizzy-haired gal. And what the hell do the two of them need with two cases of Jack Daniel's? But over the weeks it took to build the house, a kind of unspoken country respect and affection grew between the little town and the young couple.

And build the house they did. They changed their minds about John Norman's traditional room plan and designed, together, a new, radical structure. It was to be an irregular, six-sided adobe house, spaciously wide along the front and two sides, narrowing toward the back, where the kitchen was to be. The roof sloped from front to back; the interior was open except for a loft bedroom in the front and a central fireplace, open to both sides. The floors were red tile, and there would be windows on both sides to bring the desert indoors.

John Norman hired a crew of local good ol' boys and started to work. They were a bit wary of him at first—what could a city fella know about building a house? But they came to like and trust him, because he worked harder than any of them. Though they thought it was going to be the funniest-looking house they ever saw, they followed their orders. Hell, they were gettin' paid good wages!

Esther worked, too, right alongside the men, and although they were embarrassed by her presence at first, they soon got past that discomfort. The very first time she hit her thumb with a hammer and hollered "Goddamn shit!" they started to treat her like one of the boys.

In no time, the well was sunk and the windmill erected. The cattle were delivered, along with the motorcycles to herd them with. Work on the house went quickly, though the roof was a real innovation: log beams extending from the back to beyond the front of the house, covered with solar heating panels, alternated with stained glass they had designed and fabricated in Taos, New Mexico. The solar panels, ordered from Denver, fascinated the good ol' boys. They learned a lot from John Norman about the principles of solar energy while that roof went up.

One day, as John Norman and his crew worked on the roof, he saw Esther roll up in the old flatbed, which was crammed with odds and ends of rustic frontier furniture. He jumped down from the roof, nails jangling in his carpenter's apron. He was stripped to the waist, his tan, well-muscled body gleaming with sweat. The hard work had been like a tonic to him. He hadn't looked or felt this healthy in ten years. Though he was still boozing some, he was off hard drugs completely.

"What's that?" he demanded as Esther climbed down from the cab. "We don't even have floors yet."

Esther, too, was deeply tanned and fit looking. She had taken to country life with the enthusiasm that only a city girl can muster. Today she wore short shorts, a work shirt, plaid knee socks, and engineer boots. Every inch the homesteading woman. Now, with satisfaction, she inspected her newly acquired furniture.

"You know me—instant gratification. Who needs floors?"

"Where'd you get it all?" John Norman asked.

"Oh, around."

"Esther. Where'd you get it? You've been gone all day."

"Well, if you must know, I drove from ranch to ranch and politely asked the ladies of the territory if perchance they had any old furniture they wished to part with for a reasonable amount of cash."

"Girl," he said, shaking his head, "you are somethin' else."

By sunset, she had set out a perfect table for two in the front yard, complete with crystal, linen, wine, and elegant antique chairs. They sat watching the sun go down, sipping wine and dining on bread, fruit, and cheese. Smiling at each other, holding hands across the tablecloth, they knew that they had never been so happy, perhaps would never be as happy again.

Soon the house was finished. Esther furnished it, simply but beautifully, with her second-hand furniture, decorating the walls with colorful Indian hanging and old photographs of homesteaders of long ago. Much of the furniture John Norman built of raw wood. Their bed was constructed of pine logs, the dining table of oak planking with log legs. It was a warm, friendly home, and very much their own. Except for trips to town, they saw no one. They never called Los Angeles, refusing even to read the papers, although they knew that Esther's album was soon to be released. They were a pair of latter-day pioneers, and they loved every minute of it.

John Norman tended his cattle, adding slowly to the herd, and he bought a couple of horses. Hc taught Esther to ride. As always in the country, small events were a cause for celebration—the birth of the first calf, the first sprouts in Esther's vegetable garden.

While John Norman played rancher, Esther attacked housewifery with gusto. She taught herself to garden and to sew. She built terrariums until it seemed they would take over the house. She became a passable cook, but that wasn't enough; she decided to teach herself to bake.

She sat alone in her kitchen one afternoon, surrounded by masses of what she hoped would become rising dough, Volume Two of Julia Child propped before her. A fine coat of flour covered everything. Esther was not able to maintain neatness in the kitchen; ingredients seemed to run away with her. As always when she cooked, she carried on a running dialogue with herself.

"Why, Esther"—this in a falsetto voice—"you say you made this bread yourself?"

"Of course I made this bread myself," she replied in her own voice, as if she were doing a TV commercial, "I made it with the sourdough starter I got from an Eskimo roadie." A bell rang and she rushed to the oven, pausing over a bowl of lumpy dough. "Get back there," she snarled, poking it. *"Down."* Removing a pathetic, misshapen loaf from the oven, she frowned and went back to Julia Child.

" 'If your loaves seem below standard,' " she read aloud primly, " 'go over the instructions in Step Nine.' Actually, Julia m'dear, I skipped Step Nine."

Behind her, something flared up suddenly in the fireplace, belching smoke out into the room. "My God!" she shrieked, grabbing the broiler rack with a towel and racing with its sputtering, flaming cargo to the door. Running into the yard, yelling "Fire! Fire!," she almost knocked over John Norman, who was about to enter the house. She hurled the fiery object out into the yard and stood screaming at it. A startled John Norman grabbed a shovel and beat out the flames while Esther stood rooted to the spot, her hands covering her eyes.

"You were so brave. You killed it before it could get us," she fluttered at John Norman. Her hug coated him from head to toe with flour.

"What was it?" John Norman looked over his shoulder at the dead object.

"The steaks we were going to have for dinner," she said. "My God, I thought the house would go!"

"Wow, Esther!" John Norman shook his head in doleful amazement. Who but Esther could create a holocaust merely out of two little steaks?

They started into the house together.

"I love to cook," Esther said. "When we go on tour I have to have a kitchen in every motel room. I want to practice. I want to be able to cook with my *soul*. Some women cook with their soul. It's beautiful!"

"What do you mean when *we* go on the road?" he asked as they entered the back door.

"Aren't we?"

"Not together, we're not," he answered, turning away and dropping her hand.

"Why not? Three reasons," she challenged.

"One, I don't want to. Two, I don't want to. Three, I don't want to." He kissed her gently but firmly, patted her on the fanny, and went back out the door.

On the kitchen table, the timer rang, reminding Esther that it was Julia Child time. She looked forlornly at her bowls of dough. "Why don't you guys take five?" she said.

The pattern of their life at the ranch was beautiful—simple, clean. Their peace remained undisturbed, troubled only occasionally by the real world of music and tours and money and managers and albums and concert dates. Esther thought of her burgeoning career often, but rarely spoke of it. She knew what John Norman's reaction would be, and it unsettled her and frightened her. Almost every trace of his old self-destructive urges had disappeared since they had been at the ranch. The hard outdoor work, the early hours, and the regular meals had made a new man of him. Sometimes Esther would forget what he used to be like. Forget, say the wrong thing, and set off a minor explosion.

Whenever she tried to talk to him about their going on tour together, John Norman would leave the room on some pretext. Often, he would climb on his big motorcycle and head off, riding across the desert at high speed, to be gone for hours.

One rainy day they were picnicking in bed on fruit and cheese, as they sometimes did, opening a dozen absurd and expensive wedding presents that had finally found their way to them from the gang in Los Angeles. They were a little stoned, playing silly games, both feeling good. Esther was feeding John Norman strawberries by putting them one at a time between her lips and kissing them away into his mouth. The presents made her think of L.A. and her album. She kept intending to get back to her career, but she was afraid for John Norman. She knew they couldn't stay forever in this primitive fantasy world; she knew reality would intrude, and soon. And she knew that her career was important to her, that nothing must stand in the way.

"Listen," she said, getting up from the bed. "I want you always to do what you want, okay?"

"I like to watch you eat," John Norman said. "I've never seen anything like it. You put your whole heart and soul and back and everything else in it."

"You like me, huh?" she said.

He was examining a large, leatherbound book he had just unwrapped. "Look at this—a wedding present from Brian, which appears to be . . ."

Esther pressed on. "We could do our whole tour in trash flash." She dangled a fancy dress in front of her. "You could get a matching guitar strap."

"Your tour, not mine, babe," he said flatly, still examining the book. "Oh, a very rare, hand-illuminated, sixteenth-century edition of the Kama Sutra."

"We could've used a toaster," said Esther.

He held up a beautiful hand-cut crystal decanter. "Can you imagine somebody sending us an empty bottle?"

"I sent it," she said, holding up the gossamer top of a white pants suit.

"That won't work under the lights," he said.

"I'm not going to plan my life around the lights," she said.

"Oh, yes, you are," he said. "You haven't earned the right not to—not yet, anyway."

"You don't know how I hate that attitude," she said, seizing the opening she'd been waiting for. "You think you can tell me how to do it, but you won't do it yourself. Please do it, Johnny. Please do the tour with me."

He was slipping into his jeans and shirt.

"You're a sweet baby," he said, trying to hold in his temper. "But I ain't gonna do it."

Esther was angry now, too. She was getting sick of his refusals. She knew his fears—at least, she felt she understood them. What she couldn't stand was his childish refusal to deal with them head on. She knew he could handle it, with her help.

"Either you do this tour with me, or goddamn it, I won't do it," she shouted. "I'll stay home and bake bread and we'll get fat and our teeth'll fall out."

"That'll be terrific, Esther, 'cause you're so good around the kitchen!" He said it almost fiercely, barely able to control himself, and she was shocked by the undertone of resentment in his voice.

John Norman pulled on his boots and stomped out of the house, slamming the door behind him. Numb, Esther continued to play with the white tunic. From outside, above the sound of the rain, she heard the roar of a motorcycle. She ran to a window.

"Oh, for God's sake!" she yelled. She hurried into the white suit and rushed out.

John Norman was riding his cycle through a barrel

course he had set up. With the throttle wide open, he was skidding crazily in the mud, slipping, turning, barely able to keep the machine upright. It's my fault, Esther thought, I shouldn't have said anything. He was off his rocker again, off on his own private little death trip. It scared her when he was like this, but it made her angry, too. She ran after him, shouting, but he eluded her. Esther knew that in this mood he was perfectly capable of running her down.

Out of breath and soaked to the skin, she was nevertheless determined to bring him back inside the house. "Love and cherish, huh?" she yelled over the rain and the roar of the bike. "How are you going to cherish me in traction?"

He ignored her, twisting and turning the heavy cycle, driving like a maniac.

"You get yourself paralyzed from the neck down," she went on, "how do you think we're ever going to have a baby? You bastard!" She shook her fist at him.

Suddenly the motorbike flew out from under John Norman. He somersaulted to the ground and lay without moving. Esther stood stock still for a long moment, terrified, holding her breath.

"John Norman?" she called softly at last, not daring to raise her voice. Then she ran to kneel beside him in the mud, ignoring the expensive white outfit she was wearing. Her heart stopped in her breast as she touched his still face. And then, he opened his eyes and grinned up at her.

"I thought you were dead!" she yelled, furious with him. "Don't do that to me! You know what you did to me?"

She slapped him hard, hurting her hand. John Norman tried to grab her, laughing at her fear.

"I'll never die!" he shouted gleefully. "I'm too pretty to die!"

Esther struggled, hitting out at him savagely. Avoiding her fists, he tried to kiss her. Rolling and punching, they were like two young animals, their fighting and lovemaking all mixed up together. They were soon both soaked and covered with mud.

"Bullshit!" Esther panted. "What's wrong with you? You only feel alive when you're scaring yourself half to death?" She broke away from him.

"If you're afraid to die, you're afraid to live," he laughed, reaching for her. She backed farther away, glaring at him like an angry cat.

"Not me. I like life too much."

John Norman grabbed for her again, pretending that it was all a joke, trying to tickle her and make her laugh.

"Quit that!" demanded Esther. "Life is so lousy with me you want to die?"

"Hold still!" he ordered, trying to pin her underneath him for a kiss.

"I will not! I don't like hairy men!" She twisted away, avoiding his face.

Shouting, "I'll shave it off," John Norman turned and ran for the house. A startled Esther ran after him.

"What are you doing . . . John Norman!" She ordered him to come back.

But John Norman stalked into the house. He found a pair of scissors and was raising them to his face, about to shear off his beard, when Esther raced in and seized his arm. They grappled for the scissors, half seriously, half in fun.

"You damn fool! Don't!" she yelled. "How would I recognize you? Please don't. I wouldn't know what you looked like."

Now they were on the floor together in front of the fireplace, wrestling like bear cubs. Relenting, John Norman handed over the scissors, and they both lay back, wet and exhausted.

"Oh, don't," Esther pleaded in a small, sad voice. "Please. Don't leave me alone. I'm afraid of the dark.'" He looked at her for a long moment, then bent over and kissed her gently.

"If you die," she whispered, "I'll kill you."

"Oh, hell," he sighed, resigned, "I'll go on the goddamn tour."

Jubilant, Esther threw her arms around John Norman's neck, hardly able to believe her ears.

For days after that, she talked about nothing but the tour—planning, scheming, fantasizing. But then she realized that she was trying too hard to believe that it was really going to happen; she knew that John Norman's heart really wasn't in it. There was no kindling, no spark of enthusiasm. His response was lifeless. When he talked with her about the tour, it was with reluctance, and there was something akin to dread in his voice.

Yet, she kept pressing him. She had faith that a joint tour would be the best thing that could happen to John Norman. To both of them. One day, as they took the horses out for an early morning ride, she pressed again.

"Do you realize how long it's been since you've seen anyone but me?" she asked.

"Yeah, I like it," he said slowly. "It gives the day a focus. I get up in the morning, I see you. I go to sleep at night, I see you. It's simple." He turned to her. "I can handle it."

Esther felt a melting sensation in her heart. God, she loved this man! If only . . . Her expression clouded. Why won't he *talk* to me? Why won't he face up to what we have to do—meet the rest of the world on its own turf and beat it? Johnny, she thought, it could be so easy for us if you would let it be. Life isn't a contest you have to win all by yourself. Nobody's up there keeping score on how macho you are. Let me help you, John Norman, don't be ashamed to take help from me. I'm your wife; I love you. Talk to me, Johnny, let me talk to you one to one. Deal with me, baby, be up front with me as I am with you. You know I'm not like all the others. You must have known that, or you wouldn't have married me. You love me; I can feel it. I take from you, baby, why won't you take something from me? Or, at least, why won't you let me give it?

But she choked back the questions and remained silent. Because she knew that if she began to ask them, he would turn away again, perhaps for good this time.

Chapter IX

As the weeks went by, Esther continued to keep after John Norman about the tour. She persuaded him to work on her music with her, because he refused to play his own. He spent a lot of time coaching her, working out instrumental arrangements for her songs. He even ordered another Moog synthesizer, had it shipped to the ranch, and began to teach her how to play it. All this was very painful for him, she knew, but she continued to lead him gently, and he reluctantly followed. He was beginning to drink again, not as heavily as before, but too heavily for Esther's liking. And, though he tried not to show it, he was sullen most of the time. Esther refused to deal with these warning signs, because she hoped and prayed that they would go away. She kept talking about the future, the tour. Goddamn it, it was going to work! She would *make* it work!

Inch by inch, Esther attempted to lead John Norman back to the reality that lay beyond their ranch-house. And then one day reality arrived all of a sudden, like a bomb, exploding their private world, crashing into their home like an invading army.

Esther was in the kitchen, happily baking bread. Having finally mastered Julia's recipe, she now baked with a vengeance. John Norman kept saying that there was so much fresh bread in the house, they should feed it to the cattle. He was crouched now in the living room, working on the Moog; the synthesizer stood with its back off, wires and parts scattered all about him. Hearing a low, distant sound of engines, Esther looked out of the kitchen window. In the distance, three long black Cadillac limousines were twisting their way up the dry gulch, raising huge clouds of dust through which they were only intermittently visible. Oh, God, Esther thought, here come the Sherman tanks. Here comes the outside world.

"John Norman," she called into the living room, "guess who's coming to dinner?"

It was the entire crew—Brian, Danziger, Bobby Ritchie, Freddy—all of them looking out of place and faintly ridiculous in the middle of the Arizona desert in their Los Angeles getups. Soon they were all over the little house, yelling greetings, moving furniture around, playing hot new music on an expensive tape deck.

Brian, of course, was not to be separated from his precious telephone. Knowing that there wasn't one on the ranch, he carried a radio-phone in his Gucci attaché case. Instantly, he began placing calls. It was his addiction; he was never so happy as when long-distance wires were connecting him to somewhere very far away. Danziger had brought along a famous jet-set photographer, who was accompanied by a costumer with bags of clothing. Freddy opened a portfolio of sketches and immediately spread them around the house. She had a production designer in tow, but he never uttered a word. He just looked around him curiously, as though wondering who had designed *this* set.

The photographer, whose name was Nikki, moved around the room shooting with a 35-mm strobe-synched camera, the strobe units flashing into little white umbrella diffusers. Every time she shot, the entire room lit up in a blinding flash. And she shot a great many times, blinding everybody, adding immeasurably to the hysteria inside the little house. Nikki was painfully skinny, unnaturally pale. She looked as though she had spent her life locked in a damp basement.

Esther, who was rather enjoying this, lay on the couch, her head cradled in John Norman's lap. She was listening, but John Norman wasn't. He never could get used to all these people; they made his head ache. It was bedlam after the peace and idyllic quiet of the last few weeks.

"Ignore me," Nikki kept saying, as she moved around them, shooting constantly from every conceivable angle. "Pretend I don't exist." Click. Flash. "Pretend I am a Japanese servant in a Japanese play . . ." Click. Flash.

Esther and John Norman exchanged grins, rolling their eyes at each other. From the bedroom in the loft above, Brian's voice rose as he shouted into the radio-phone in German.

"Darlings," gushed Freddy breathlessly, "you don't know what's happened while you've been gone!"

"*. . . die Geschichte der Karte*, Brian Wexler," Brian was shouting.

"Who's he talking to?" Esther asked, wincing with each flash of the strobe.

"Budapest," said Freddy. "We've got number-one acceptance to the tour."

"Jerzy? Brian," Wexler continued into the phone. "*Aber eine Karte ist mehr . . . aber es wachst auch der Bob Dylan?*"

"He talks to cities?" Esther asked. "Not to people?"

"Sometimes to governments," John Norman said.

"*Keine Zeit der Geschichte, das* . . . Where the fuck are we?" Brian yelled down.

"Arizona," John Norman shouted.

"*Das ist Arizona.* Cowboys *und* Indians," Brian shouted into the phone. "How do you say 'split the publishing' in German?" he yelled down again.

"If he's talking to Budapest, Hungarian is the language he's looking for," Esther said, covering her eyes as Nikki snapped a couple of blinding close-ups.

"We've got her booked for thirty-eight days," Freddy began, "and they're—"

"Booked where?" Esther asked, sitting up. Now she was interested, vitally interested.

"They're sending checks for advances against the guarantees. And we've got a TV special already lined up," Fredy went on. Brian hung up and made his way gingerly down the narrow stairs.

"Say what you want about communists," he said, shaking his head in admiration, "those guys really know how to structure a deal."

The strobe popped away as Nikki crouched for one shot, stood on a chair for another. "Sometimes I work with an assistant," she said to no one in particular, "but with another body you intrude distracting presences . . . Forget me! Forget me!"

"What's the billing?" Esther asked.

Ritchie, who had been fooling with the Moog, looked up. He, Freddy, Brian, and Gary looked at each other, then at John Norman. There was silence.

Esther looked at them, misreading their bewilderment. "Over here, gang. *She* spoke. 'What's the billing?' she asked."

"The billing?" Freddy said haltingly. "Why, I think just—"

"I want John Norman first," Esther said emphatically.

Tension filled the little room, infecting everyone except Esther. This was the first time it had occurred to any of them, except her and John Norman, that they would tour together. Together? Pair this bright new star with the most notorious fuck-up in the business? Commercial suicide. Even their music was different. Brian looked at John Norman, who nodded and got up. They both moved toward the front door.

"We want every fifth day off," Esther said.

"What would you do on a day off in North Tonawanda, love?" Freddy jumped in, drawing Esther's attention from the departing men. "Why not just make more lovely money?"

Outside, Brian and John Norman stood in silence. Brian squinted into the sun. John Norman looked at the ground, toeing the dust.

"Esther looks great," Brian said. "She looks happy. I'm happy for her." He looked up at John Norman. "Happy for you."

"Speak up, Brian. You don't have to go out in the fresh air and open country to say that," John Norman said dryly.

"I mean it," Brian said. "You seem a little like somebody I knew a long time ago. It's good." Despite all the trouble he'd caused, John Norman was still someone Brian cared deeply for, and this was painful for him.

"You don't want her touring with old Doctor Trouble," John Norman said. He was making it easy for his manager, almost as if he wanted this to happen.

"I hope you remember I'm talking as a man who loves you and Esther," Brian said gently. "She's got her own music, her own public—they want *her*. You they're sueing. Why should she have to pick up on that?"

"Jesus, Brian, why don't you just come out and say it?" John Norman was not even putting up a fight.

"Can you take it?" Brian asked.

"Better from you than readin' it in the papers," John Norman said, still staring at the ground.

Brian sighed and straightened his shoulders. This was the speech he'd been dreading. Could John Norman *really* take it?

"Your songs don't flash," he said matter-of-factly. "You're sloppy, people get hurt. Her single is number six with a bullet, she's got a good shot at a Grammy. The album will take off soon; Warner is backing us all the way." He paused, searching for the right words. "She's ready to fly on her own. Let her go."

John Norman shoved his hands in his jeans pockets and looked away at the desert. "Yeah, well," he said, "It's what I been tryin' to tell her, her music and mine don't go on the same stage . . ."

Brian winced. He felt his guts knotting up.

"Maybe you could produce the tour," he suggested without conviction.

"Me? Her producer?" John Norman's laugh had a bitter tinge to it. "I'm a music man," he said. "I'll call Lee and Pete, get up some new songs. Time to create some bright new tomorrows . . ." His voice trailed off.

"Listen . . . ah . . ." Brian began apologetically.

"Don't worry, Brian." John Norman turned to face him now. "I'll tell Esther." Like hell I will, he thought.

They returned in silence to the house, where Nikki was still shooting away at an annoyed Esther.

"I'm getting something I like very, very much," the photographer murmured.

"Freddy?" Brian went to get her. "I want you to come outside and look at this goddamned sunset."

"I saw a sunset once," said Freddy. "It was so good I never needed to see another."

"Out here, Freddy," ordered Brian firmly. "You won't believe this." Finally taking the hint, Freddy reluctantly followed him out of doors, followed by Gary and Bobby to whom Brian had also beckoned.

It was obvious to Esther that something was up, but she thought it best not to press about it. Whatever it was, she would deal with it when she had to. She gave her attention to John Norman, eager to tell him her latest.

"I've got a terrific idea for the middle of the set," she said.

"Yeah," he said morosely, "well, I want to talk to you about that.

Esther shot him an apprehensive look, steeling herself for something unpleasant. We shouldn't have let the outside world come in here, she thought. It was a mistake. We should have gone to it, hand in hand. Then, whatever unhappiness it brought, we might have licked it.

They stood staring at each other, ten feet apart, with Nikki snapping and buzzing around them like an annoying flying insect. She was shooting only Esther now.

"I should have brought an assistant to do this," jabbered the photographer. "But you never know, sometimes it spoils the mood . . . one more body around . . ."

"You've changed your mind," Esther said to John Norman, her voice flat, drained of emotion. She searched his face for an answer, but he could not look her in the eye.

"And when I shoot somebody the first time," the photographer rattled on, moving to within a foot of Esther. "Almost ready here . . ."

"You're not going to do the tour," Esther accused. What had happened outside with Brian? What had Brian said to him?

"Esther," John Norman began, "I thought about it. I want you to do it alone. If I'm on the bill, you'll never know if you can do it alone." He paused, wetting his dry lips, and looked at her earnestly. Was he getting through? Christ, he hoped so!

Esther stared back at him, her eyes narrowed, her brow furrowed in pain. She looked as though she had just been slapped.

"Do the TV thing they're talking about while I get a few together with Lee," John Norman continued rapidly. "When you tour, I'll be your groupie if you'll be mine." He managed a weak smile.

"All right, got it," Nikki said, her camera popping away.

Esther turned and looked blankly into the camera as the photographer moved in for tight close-ups.

"I don't want people to say I'm carrying you, babe," John Norman said lamely. She still would not look at him.

"Good . . . Good. . . ," Nikki said, "we've almost got it . . ."

"Since when did you care what people say?" Esther said slowly, calmly.

"I care what people say about you," John Norman said.

"I'm scared of going out alone," she said in the same flat voice. "I'm scared of going public."

"You've already gone," he said gently.

She looked at him now, her face suddenly revealing her pain and vulnerability.

"Esther!" Nikki said urgently, "Beautiful! Look here, quick." She snapped away. "Fabulous," she exulted. "Fabulous!"

Chapter X

And so she went back that day with Brian, Freddy, and the rest of them. John Norman knew, she knew, that something had ended. There was no point in pretending it hadn't, no point in dragging out the agony. She knew she could never give up her career for him or anybody else; he knew he could not go with her or stand in her way—it was time for a new beginning for both of them. She was exhilarated about the future, but frightened, too, of being without him. Not just afraid to be alone, but afraid for him, of what he might do. He was happy for her, of course. What would he do with himself, she wanted to know. Well, he reckoned he'd stay at the ranch for a while, work on his music, look after the place. He'd come to her soon. She made him promise to put in a telephone. No, he said, I'll call from town. We agreed—no phones.

And so they lived for the next few weeks—apart for the first time since their marriage. She settled into the Hollywood house and threw herself into her career, working on a new album, composing, negotiating with lawyers, agents, publicity people, and preparing for her television special, which was entitled simply "Esther." And she loved every minute of it. She found that she had a good head for business, better than most performers. As with any newcomer, the vultures swarmed around her, expecting another easy victim. But she was tough and firm. Brian was deeply impressed. He told her she was good, damn good, she could manage herself almost as well as he could do it for her. But he offered his services anyway. "Brian," she said, "I trust you. Draw up a contract and I'll sign it. I don't think you'd ever cross me."

Esther worried about John Norman, cursing their "no-phone" pact, staying home every night she could, waiting to hear from him. Usually he didn't call—or had he called when she wasn't home? How could she tell? Nothing was nothing. When they did speak, he sounded all right—a little down maybe, always a little smashed, but cheerful enough. For the first time, she hated the telephone. *Goddamn* disembodied voices! When she asked him about the new music, he was evasive. Going all right, he'd say. All right. "What was it like, she wanted to know. "Oh . . . different," he'd say. Mostly ballads, mostly slow, rather sad stuff. He would never tell her any more than that.

Every time they talked, she would beg him to join her. She needed him now, when could he come? Couldn't he work in L.A., where they could be together again? Couldn't they pursue their separate careers while being together? "I need you, Johnny," she pleaded, but he was evasive, always putting her off.

Yet, finally, he did come. She met him at the airport in the Ferrari. Ecstatic, she threw her arms around him tightly, hugging and kissing him. He returned her kisses, glad to see her, but he seemed a little embarrassed by the greeting, and more than a little groggy, too. She was sure she could smell the booze on him, and wondered if he was doing downers again as well. Yet he looked healthy, tanned, and clear-eyed. He gave her one of his best heartwarming, boyish grins. Damn! he was glad to see her, he thought.

Esther was late for a rehearsal at the television studio, she apologized. Could he drop her off and then they'd have a real reunion at the Angelo Drive house later? Sure, why not? He planned to drop by the Record Plant and check in with the band, anyway.

As they zoomed down Sunset Boulevard past the line of billboards that announced the latest albums and concert dates of the biggest musical groups and stars, they saw one of John Norman Howard and the Speedway. It was old and peeling, left over from the aborted tour. Another one, close by, just going up, was of Esther Hoffman, promoting her album and announcing the TV special. It was a full-face close-up, the last shot of Esther that Nikki had taken at the ranch. A vulnerable, haunting woman's face. A star's face, thought John Norman.

The Ferrari pulled up at the studio. The marquee outside announced the upcoming special program, starring "The Sensational Esther Hoffman." Without giving it a second glance, Esther got out of the car.

"Jesus," she said plaintively to John Norman, "what am I gonna do without you for six whole hours?"

"I'll write," he promised, laughing.

"Give the guys a hug from me," she laughed back, kissing him.

She was at the studio door when he called out to her. "Esther. . . ?"

She came back to the car and looked at him quizzically.

"What?" she asked.

He smiled. "Nothing," he said. "I just wanted another look at you."

She stood still for a minute as the Ferrari pulled away, a worried expression on her face. Was he all right? Together? She shook off the uneasiness and plunged into the studio.

John Norman headed for the Record Plant, where the Speedway was working. When he'd called Bobby from Arizona, the roadie had been vague about what the band was up to, but he had urged John Norman to come by as soon as he got in.

As he strode into the building and down the hall, John Norman was greeted with subdued hellos and wary welcomes by the staff. More than once in fits of stoned, drunken madness, he had trashed this place and the Plant's facility up north in Sausalito. At one hundred and fifty dollars an hour, he had often run up enormous bills without ever laying down a single track. Though he always paid for the time and the damages, John Norman was considered, as one engineer put it, "not worth the fucking hassle." In fact, he was both welcomed and dreaded for the same reasons at studios all over the world—the Blue Door and Media Sound in New York, Criteria in Miami, Kaye-Smith in Seattle, Caribou Ranch in Colorado. He had been banned from both Island Studios in London, where he had destroyed some $50,000 worth of equipment, and the Muscle Shoals Studio in Alabama, where the chief engineer had locked him out. ("Southern hospitality just don't go far enough to cover you, motherfucker!") Yet there had been a time when he'd been clean, straight, and businesslike. And a star.

Like most such places, the L.A. Record Plant was a stately pleasure dome, with every possible convenience available to the musicians. Though the décor ran to stark functionalism, there was an understated luxury about the place—first-class reclining airline seats to fall out in; a well-stocked bar and refrigerator; a stereo system with every imaginable tape and record; a separate lounge with foam-padded floor, electronic games, and pinball machines. Beyond the sliding glass doors a flagstone patio, furnished with the best and most comfortable outdoor furniture, adjoined a huge Jacuzzi in which tired musicians could refresh themselves.

John Norman made his way to the glass-enclosed control booth. The console on which the engineer and the producer controlled the input and output to each of the tape channels was as sophisticated as any in the world. Stretching twelve feet across the booth, the console was covered with a bewildering array of dials, gauges, switches, pushbuttons, and a somewhat anachronistic tangle of patch cords, similar to those on an old fashioned switchboard, which controlled the input to the twenty-four separate channels on the master tape. The console was as modern as the dashboard of a jumbo jet; as much as can be done to an individual sound, it could do. It could make sound louder, add echo, position it in various places along the left-to-right stereo spectrum, modify its timbre, and correct it so that the volume remained consistent across various frequencies. It could put each musician's part onto a separate channel of tape, allowing one instrument's errors to be erased without affecting the others.

Bobby Ritchie was in the control room with two engineers and a couple of girls. In the studio, the Speedway was just finishing a number. Lee and Pete were rapping with a newcomer, an ugly, remarkably scruffy little guy John Norman didn't recognize.

Bobby greeted him effusively. "If it isn't Amelia Earhart!" he shouted, throwing his arms around John Norman. He opened the studio mikes, and the grinning band members moved to the glass and shouted greetings.

"No, it's her navigator," John Norman said. "What's happenin', gang?"

"Jesus," Lee said, "does he look healthy!"

"He must be on unemployment!" Bobby Ritchie kidded. Taking his finger off the talkback switch, he turned to John Norman. "What do you think of the sound?" he asked, referring to the just completed set.

"What is it?"

"A new Freeway album—that's what we've been workin' on," Richie replied triumphantly. This was his moment of triumph. He was producing it himself. It was called simply "Freeway." No John Norman. No hassles. Everything going smoothly, for a change. I'll never be able to thank Esther enough, he thought.

"We got a release date in three weeks," he continued. "Nothing changes but the changes." He couldn't resist that one.

"Freeway?" John Norman was bewildered. It wasn't sinking in. He felt as though he were walking in a dense fog. "What the hell's a Freeway?"

Ritchie pointed to the band. "Their single goes to number five with a bullet this week," he said proudly. It was *his* band now. "Hottest thing in rock and roll." No more Speedway; no more John Norman Howard Speedway.

"How's Esther?" asked Dallas through his open mike. "She's chasin' us right up the charts . . ."

"Esther's terrific," John Norman said automatically. "She put off the tour so she could do a TV thing. She's ready for the road. She's doin' another Indian Relief Benefit."

"Hey, I think we're doin' that damn thing, too," Pete said.

"Did you hear what we were doin' when you came in?" asked Lee.

"No, just the end."

"Remember the song, 'You and Me?' Started to write it after the Memphis gig? I got hung up finishing it. Keppel came up with a verse that tied it all together. Hey!" Lee interrupted himself and pointed to the scruffy kid. "You don't even know Keppel. Keppel, meet John Norman Howard."

"How are you, sir?" the kid said shyly.

"Keppel's the new baby of the group," Lee said.

"I had to buy all of your goddamn records about

five times, 'cause my ol' man would steal 'em and th'ow 'em out, I played 'em so much," Keppel said in a soft Alabama drawl. "It's a real kick in the ass to meet you."

"Down, boy," Pete said.

"Well, I'm indebted to you." John Norman was dazed; he couldn't think of anything to say. "You guys been on the road?"

"They don't have radio in Arizona?" Ritchie said. "Where the hell have you been, man?" He had set up this encounter, and now he could tell from John Norman's expression that it was working beautifully. Revenge is sweet, he thought.

"I had my radio off for about a minute," John Norman said. He paused to grope for words. "Listen, that's fantastic. Take it and run."

"I hate to break this up, boys, but time is money," Ritchie said, basking in his producer's role. "Let's cut this turkey and bullshit later. Pete, you're laying back on that solo. If you're gonna show it, show it hard. Otherwise, keep it in your pants."

"Hey, man, listen to this," Lee said to John Norman. "You're gonna love it." He was trying to hide his embarrassment. They all were. They owed that man in there a lot.

"Well, lay it on me," John Norman said. They started into the number. The style, the tempo—everything—was different from the old John Norman Howard sound. After a few bars Ritchie turned down the sound and offered cocaine in a spoon. John Norman coked up, taking several good snorts.

"When the hell did all this happen?" he asked.

"You gotta understand they couldn't wait," Bobby Ritchie said, still holding the spoon under John Norman's nose. This is the last time I spoon-feed this baby, he thought. "The world couldn't wait while you were off doin' your number with the chick. We had a single chasin' Esther right up the charts. You really never listened to the radio out there?"

"Not if I could help it," John Norman said, snorting deeply, pulling the coke into his head. Whammo! Good snow, he thought. His eyes brightened. He felt better. "Hey, man, come on, walk me out," he said. Leaving the booth, he moved briskly down the corridor, Ritchie trailing him. He felt good. Relieved, almost. Sure, it was the coke, but it was more than that . . . At the door, he turned. Ritchie and he looked at each other in silence.

"Listen. . . ," Ritchie began, but John Norman held up his hand as if to say: Don't try to explain, man.

Ritchie knew he had to leave it alone, that it was all over for John Norman Howard and the Speedway. They both knew it. Suddenly, Ritchie threw his arms around his ex-boss and hugged him hard.

"I love you, man," he said, his voice cracking. John Norman pulled away and smiled. He put his hands on his former roadie's shoulders.

"You do good, now," he said quietly. Then he turned and left.

Bobby Ritchie stood for a moment, watching John Norman move across the lot to his car. His mind was racing at top speed from the coke. He remembered all his years with the Speedway. How he, a junior equipment man with a second rate L.A. band, had been picked by John Norman to be chief roadie. It was just after the Speedway's "discovery" by Brian, and this would be the first big tour to promote the band's first album. He had panicked. He'd never had so much responsibility, and it scared hell out of him. But John Norman had stood by him, taught him everything he knew—which was plenty—backed him up all the way. At first, Ritchie remembered, his boss had insisted on knowing every detail, personally okaying every decision. John Norman was tough in those days—quick, smart, sure of himself. Yeah, he drank and doped, but so did they all when they weren't working. He played as hard as he worked, and when he worked, it was all out. He had the self-assurance of a rising star on the make. He was cold and impersonal, sometimes frighteningly so. He knew his goals and let nothing and no one distract him. John Norman was also extraordinarily generous with his people. Understanding the value of a loyal staff, he never failed to reward those who gave that little extra. Bobby Ritchie had been his favorite because Ritchie, was the best. Soon, Ritchie was practically running the band himself on the road. Those early years had been fabulous for all of them.

Ritchie couldn't recall exactly when it started to fall apart. John Norman began to drink more heavily. He got into that lethal combination of booze, downs, and coke. His mood swings became more and more violent. He began to hate and fear his vast and fickle audiences, referring to them as "the creeps." Then came the fits of violent temper. Uncontrolled rages would possess him at the slightest provocation, and he would lash out at anything or anybody around. Ritchie had taken a lot of grief from the bastard—a lot of grief. But it was over now, he thought, as he watched John Norman walk away. He'd never have to take any shit off that s.o.b. again. There, he thought, goes a 24-carat loser. John Norman Howard had fought hard for his place at the pinnacle of rock. He'd earned it. Then, for some deep-seated, self-destructive reason, he had methodically destroyed it all. Thrown it away. Ritchie could never figure it out. He thought he understood just two things about John Norman Howard: he was incapable of loving anyone, and he hated himself with a frightening intensity. An abiding death wish drove John Norman relentlessly; Bobby Ritchie had seen it, even aided and abetted it. That was what the boss had wanted, and he always did what the boss said. He recalled the last verse of "Hellacious Acres." Who but a madman could write a song like that?

Go to hell
After dark
It's a sin filled city
An amusement park
And a one way ticket to the other side
It's a Dr. Jekyll it's a Mr. Hyde
Get down and study suspicion and doubt
At Hellacious Acres
Listen mischief makers
Admission's free you pay to get out

Chapter XI

It was late evening when John Norman gunned the Ferrari up the narrow drive to his Hollywood home, the two guard dogs racing alongside, yelping. The grounds were immaculate now, he noticed as he passed two Japanese gardeners toiling away in a lush flowerbed. He screeched to a stop at the front door, and the dogs circled the car, still barking. John Norman slumped forward against the wheel, not moving. The dogs began to whine and wag their tails. At last they slunk away.

John Norman pulled himself together and got out of the car. The coke rush had worn off now, and he moved slowly, head down, shoulders hunched, a defeated look on his face.

He entered the house. Esther had transformed it in his absence. Her elegant taste showed in every detail: beautiful Art Deco furniture, colorful rugs, newly painted walls, a thriving jungle of house plants. She had turned the old mansion into a spotless but warm and comfortable home. John Norman felt like an intruder. He made his way to the kitchen and found a frosty bottle of Stolichnaya vodka in the refrigerator. At least some things were still the same. Turning, he saw that a young black woman had entered the room. She was dressed in a service uniform—white dress, stockings, and shoes.

"Who are you?" he said.

"You want somethin', Mister Hoffman?" she said. "I'll be glad to get it for you."

He winced inwardly at "Mr. Hoffman," but his face betrayed no emotion. "No, it's okay," he said, his voice flat, weary. "I forgot anyone was here."

"Miz Hoffman called," the servant volunteered. "She said she'd be a little late, but she'd be here as soon as she can." She stood there, not quite knowing what to do. She'd never met this man before, though Mrs. Hoffman talked about him constantly and she recognized him from the numerous photographs that Esther kept in the house.

John Norman made no reply. He slammed the refrigerator shut and strolled through the house, drink in hand, ending up in his old "Playpen." Formerly a filthy hole strewn with empty bottles and beer cans, the room was now a comfortable den. He grabbed a guitar and began, softly, to pick out notes. After a few minutes, he turned on a cassette recorder and began to sing a love ballad he had been working on at the ranch. It was called "With One More Look at You."

> With one more look at you
> I could learn to tame the clouds
> And let the sun shine through
> Leave a troubled past and I might start anew . . .

The telephone rang. He ignored it. It rang on.

"Pick it up, out there!" He shouted. It kept ringing. He picked it up, irritated. "Hello? . . . No, she isn't home . . . No, this isn't her secretary . . . No, this isn't her service." Whoever was calling hung up abruptly. He looked at the receiver, shrugged, and returned to his song.

With one more look at you
I might overcome the anger
That I've learned to know . . .

The phone rang again. He glared at it, furious, but it rang on and on. Finally, he picked it up.

"Hello? No, Miss Hoffman isn't home yet." He paused, listening. "Oh, yes," he said slowly, "the reservations for the Grammy Awards . . . Well, I don't know how many will be in my wife's party. I'll have to ask her . . . Yes, certainly, we'll let you know. Goodbye." Gently, he returned the receiver to its cradle and sat there, staring into space. For a long time he did not move.

As Mo pulled the limousine up to the house, Esther spotted the Ferrari. She ran into the house, excited. "John Norman? How did it go? How's Lee?"

She was dressed in rehearsal clothes—jeans and a work shirt—but she looked good. Success obviously agreed with her; she glowed with energy.

John Norman was in the living room. He had dragged the Moog in there and had its back off, so that he could fool with the wiring. It made him less of a stranger in his own house.

"Why is it so dark in here? How can you work in the dark?" Esther ran around the huge room, turning on lights. She kissed him, still breathless and excited.

"Tell me what happened with Lee," she demanded. "When do you tour? I'll be your groupie if you'll be mine." She smiled, recalling their old joke. "Did you play your stuff for him?"

"No," he said, pretending to be absorbed in the tangled guts of the synthesizer.

"Why not?" Esther was bewildered. What had happened? Something bad had happened, she could tell.

"I don't know where their heads are at!" snorted

John Norman in disgust. "They're into some stuff now I can't get next to. I hope the hell they know what they're doing." He went on with his tinkering.

"You're not going on tour with them?" she asked in amazement.

"I don't want to talk about that," he said, looking up. "I want to talk about you. How'd it go today?"

Esther decided to let him have his way for now. He was very evidently upset, and he needed to be humored. "They hire me, and then they want to change everything. I'm too short for the costumes, too tall for the men. Too loud for the songs, too quiet for the jokes. They don't know what they want." She passed these problems off lightly, for his amusement.

John Norman smiled up at her as she stood there, feet spread a little apart, hands on hips, frowning. He loved her like this—determined, in control of herself and her career. So different from him . . .

"Yeah, right. You got to stick with yourself," he told his wife.

"I'm stickin' with *you*," she said fondly, dropping beside him on the rug and giving him a loving squeeze.

"You must be tired," he said.

"I'm starving!"

"Me, too. I want some beer and pickles."

"I want some oysters and olives and pickles."

They ran to the kitchen, racing each other, laughing and talking. One of their favorite pastimes at the ranch had been picnics in bed—elaborate spreads of expensive delicacies which they would consume like hungry wolves, after which they would make love. An orgy of food, followed by an orgy of lust, followed by an orgy of deep, exhausted sleep.

Attacking the refrigerator, Esther and John Norman pulled out and tasted fruits, vegetables, cheese, bread, wine, pickles, canned oysters, caviar, artichokes, smoked salmon. Frantic with sexual anticipation, they piled a huge tray with these goodies. John Norman sank his white teeth into a strawberry and groaned with pleasure. Biting off another piece, he kissed it into Esther's mouth. Their eyes met. He reached around her and grabbed her bottom with both hands. The telephone rang.

"Forget it!" she said, winding her arms around his waist. "Don't answer it!"

"It'll probably be for you," John Norman said.

"I don't care. Maybe they'll go away." The telephone jangled on.

"Which reminds me," he continued, letting go of her, "Jamisen called and wants to do an interview show on the twelfth. You've got a wardrobe fitting and insurance exam the day after tomorrow . . ." He ticked off the messages like a social secretary.

"Johnny, I don't want to hear about them now," she whispered, sliding her hand up his leg.

"Just let me finish before I forget. They want to know how many for your table at the Grammy Awards. And there were two hangups."

By now the telephone had stopped ringing.

John Norman smiled lopsidedly. "Who says booze and dope affect your memory? Your memory's not in your liver, anyway." His tone was bitter sarcastic, like a glass of ice water thrown in her face. The moment of closeness had passed. Could it ever be recaptured?

Esther took the phone off the hook, but it was too late; he had walked away from her. She sat down, feeling sick, sick all over, and suddenly very, very tired.

"Hey! Where are you going?" she yelled after him.

"I'm not hungry," said John Norman. "I need another drink." He left the kitchen, going to another part of the house, away from her. It was his old ploy, removing himself when things became uncomfortable for him.

Esther felt pain and worry at the same time. "What happened?" she said. "Hey, don't walk away like that, let's talk about . . ." Her voice trailed off. In another part of the house, a door slammed.

Chapter XII

The Grammy Awards ceremonies were held that year in the grand ballroom of the old Biltmore Hotel in downtown Los Angeles. As usual, anybody whose name meant something turned up, dressed to kill. The men were all in black tie, some sporting outrageously colorful ruffled shirts and printed or inky-black velvet dinner jackets. The women wore dresses from the most "in" designers. There were duplicate dresses, which provoked looks of dismay and rage.

Esther's party had a table down front, since Esther was a nominee. Brian sat there, along with Freddy, Gary, and the others. Everyone agreed that Esther looked stunning. She wore a shimmering, strapless gown in a metallic Art Deco pattern, with a matching shawl. The dress had been made from a treasured piece of antique fabric she'd picked up at a flea market years ago.

There was also general agreement that Esther was an easy win for Best New Performer of the Year. Esther herself was a nervous wreck. Not only was she feeling insecure about the award but, more important, the chair next to hers was conspicuously empty, and the ceremonies were well underway.

John Norman had been bombed by eleven that

morning. He'd left her in the afternoon, taking his tux with him, promising that he was on his way to a sauna to dry out and shape up. He would meet her at the Biltmore. He had given her his solemn oath on it. Now where was he?

Esther was angry with him, but more than angry, she was almost petrified with worry. Was he all right? Was he lying helpless somewhere? Had he gotten into a fight?

The Master of Ceremonies, Tony Orlando, announced the Best New Performer category and introduced the presenter of the award, Rita Coolidge. As they began the usual pre-announcement patter designed to build suspense, Esther scanned the room. Where in hell was John Norman? She had visions of the Ferrari smashed to bits on some freeway. Or else he's passed out in some dive, she thought. Both images made her cringe.

"So near and yet so far," Tony Orlando was saying, holding the little Grammy gramophone in his hand. "It's cruel and unusual punishment to make the have-nots give these awards to the haves. Is that fair? What happens if I decide to keep it? I think I'll fight! The winner will have to fight me—knives, bottles, guns, clubs, all the same to me. Rita, let's see who the lucky person is, and if they outweigh me . . ." She opened the envelope. Tony read it and smiled. "But first, I want to say a few words about the meaning of this award," he teased. The audience groaned good-naturedly.

Esther looked grimly straight ahead, lost in thought. Brian reached over and patted her arm, smiling.

"You're a shoo-in, baby," he said.

"Listen," she said, "I'm leaving." She tried to rise, but Brian held her back. "He's probably stuck in traffic—"

"Bullshit, Brian," she snapped. "You know better than that! He forgot."

Rita Coolidge had announced the winner, and people at adjoining tables were whispering and pointing to her.

"What?" she said.

"The winner, please," Tony Orlando beckoned. "Esther Hoffman!"

The crowd broke into enthusiastic applause. Best New Performer was always a sentimental Grammy as far as the industry was concerned, and for most of the people present, Esther was something special. She was well-known for her kindness, reasonableness, and sanity—rare qualities in any pop star, but especially in one whose career was taking off like a rocket.

Realizing she had won, Esther froze for a moment, then moved slowly up to the podium. A smiling Rita Coolidge handed her the coveted award.

"And now, I'm very pleased to present you with this Grammy as Best New Performer of the Year," Tony said.

The audience rose to its feet and gave Esther a long, thunderous ovation. As the room settled down, she spoke into the microphone.

"Thank you. Even though I didn't plan on winning this award, I must admit I did prepare a little something, just in case."

There was more applause and laughter.

"But here's the topper to that story," she went on. "I forgot it! There are two people I want to thank. Mr. Abraham Borokowski, the super of my building when I was a kid. He used to chase me out of the hall when I would sing. See, the hall had a great echo. He made me so angry that sometimes I think if he hadn't chased me, I'd still be there today."

The audience gave a shout of laughter. As it died away, Esther heard a single pair of hands clapping—loudly, slowly, rhythmically. She squinted out past the television lights to see who it was. But her heart had told her who even before she made out the face.

John Norman Howard—dead drunk, his tie undone, his evening clothes disheveled, staggered down the center aisle, still clapping. A murmur of disapproval ran through the crowd, mingled with hisses of recognition. A couple of musicians who knew him got up and grabbed for him, trying to persuade him to sit down. As Esther stood stunned a television cameraman, following excited orders from the control booth, swung his camera onto John Norman.

"Leggo my goddamn arm!" John Norman shouted, struggling to get to Esther. The audience, shocked, grew quiet, anxious not to miss a syllable. John Norman came to a stop at the foot of the stage, swaying back and forth, his arms spread.

"I'm sorry. Oh, Christ, babe! I can't find my place, they haven't got any place for me down here." He sounded like a lost, lonely little boy.

Esther reached her arms out to her husband. "And here's the other person I'd like to thank," she said in a strong, clear voice, a smile on her face. "John Norman Howard!"

He staggered up to the podium, stumbling and almost falling on the steps. "Hey, wait a minute, hey, don't do that! At least, not to me!" His speech was slurred and too loud. He gripped Esther and the podium for support, still swaying. Tony Orlando and Rita Coolidge stood by, dumbfounded and embarrassed.

"You did somethin' all by yourself and it was good; you don't owe anybody a goddamn thing for that . . . not me, not them," John Norman assured Esther, glaring at the audience.

Nobody said a word, but Brian knew what was coming. He could sense it. It's mean drunk time, he thought.

"You don't have to thank 'em for the privilege of givin' 'em somethin' good." John Norman spat the words out.

Esther watched him, her mouth dry, the palms of her hands wet, trying to think of something to say.

Now John Norman appeared to be going blank. His eyes rolled in his head; his head lolled back. Grabbing Esther by the shoulders, he blew whiskey breath in her face as he kissed her. "Gee, baby, I missed you all day," he whined.

"You're blowin' my act," she growled into his ear, reminding him of the night they met. Inside herself she was begging: John Norman, please! Please, Johnny! Pulling loose from his grasp, she turned to the audience, smiling and waving as though nothing unusual had been going on. "Good night, good night, everybody," she said, and started off the stage.

She had forgotten to take her Grammy, and John Norman picked up the little figurine from the podium and stared at it for a moment.

"Hey! You forgot the fucking bric-a-brac!" he shouted after her. "This is the award for the best. Now what about the award for the worst? You know I deserve it—and I want it. Now where the fuck is it?"

Pandemonium! Everyone was aghast. The TV monitors went blank instantly and a commercial rolled. Ushers and security men made a rush at John Norman. Esther flew to his side and began to tug him gently off the stage. Two panicked ushers grabbed him by the arms and tried to hustle him off. He pulled away, knocking their arms down. "Get your fuckin' paws off me, you apes!" he spat.

John Norman slugged one of the men hard in the gut, but the other managed to get hold of him around the neck. Brian and Freddy reached the podium, with the press and the photographers right behind them. It was turning into a real brawl. Esther found herself trapped in the middle of it, trying to defend her husband and get him out of there in one piece.

"What are you doing to him?" she yelled. "Let him alone, you bastards! Get your hands off him!" Like a mother tiger fighting to defend her cub, she began to pummel the usher who had jumped John Norman from behind. Brian tried to pull her away, but she refused to go.

With John Norman flailing, yelling, and throwing wild punches, the melee moved off the stage toward the escalator that led up and out of the ballroom. Pressing close, the photographers and film crews were eating up the action. At the bottom of the escalator, a wild swing by John Norman accidentally caught Esther full in the face. She fell onto the moving stairs. Unable to see her, John Norman fought like a crazy man to reach her, shouting her name, clawing his way up the crowded escalator.

Bebe Jesus, in a garish dinner jacket and flamboyant shirt, came barreling down the escalator with his film and sound crew. Breathless from moving down against the upward motion of the stairs, he reached Esther, who sat now with her face buried in her hands. Bebe zeroed in on her relentlessly for a close-up, then directed his camera and light men to John Norman, all the while shouting gleefully into his tape recorder. "Bebe Jesus catches all the action for you! The ex-Mister Jesus Christ Superstar belting out the new champion who happens to be his bedmate and star companion! Hey, Tarzan, how's it feel to uncork on the old lady?"

Pulling loose at last from his pursuers, John Norman reached for Esther at the top of the escalator, and Bebe Jesus moved his crew in tight for a close-up of them. It was the last straw; John Norman exploded. Picking up the little D.J., he slammed him against a wall.

"You see that?" Bebe gasped. "He's tryna' kill me! Shoot!" John Norman lunged for him again. Brian struggled to keep them apart.

"I'm suing this fucker!" Bebe Jesus screamed. The camera was still on Esther, who was attempting to shield her eyes from the lights. "Stop it!" she yelled.

"Shut off your goddamn lights! Haven't you got enough?"

John Norman stood breathing heavily now, glaring at the cowering disc jockey. Brian tried to keep back the growing crowd of curiosity seekers.

"I'm sorry, baby. I didn't mean to hurt you," John Norman said forlornly to Esther.

"I know, I know." Her voice was soothing, and she placed his arm around her shoulders to steady him. "You drink too much," she said as she led him away.

"I told you that," he said.

The crowd of gapers made way for them, still staring. "What are you looking at?" Esther demanded.

She was really angry at them now; she knew that John Norman would have left quietly if only they'd let her take care of him. Poor dopey baby, she thought.

"Take a good look," she shouted at the crowd. "Go on! None of you ever got drunk or stoned before?"

Spotting a men's room, she led the silent John Norman into it. He was still weaving from booze and exhaustion.

"Hey, don't defend me! I can take care of myself," he said.

"You're doin' a great job," she retorted. At a sink, she ran cold water on his bruised and bleeding hands. Wetting a paper towel, she washed his face and tried to straighten him out.

"What are you gonna do for an encore?" She wisecracked. "Set yourself on fire? You know what it's like watching you do this to yourself? What is it? Don't you know how good you are? What is it?"

Now she pleaded, "Is it me, Johnny? I feel so help-less." Tears came, but she held them back. "I thought everything would be perfect because we loved each other. But it's not. It isn't enough. And if we can't make it with what we've got—then what hope is there?" She paused, and saw that he was staring at his face in the mirror. "You know, Johnny," she said, "you taught me so much . . . Tell me what to do now?"

He didn't speak.

She touched him gently. "I love you," she said softly. "How come you never say that?"

He shrugged, looked down into the sink, then up at her.

"I only say it when you're asleep, babe. It's bad luck to say it out loud." He managed a weak smile.

"Then you might as well say it," she said firmly, " 'cause the luck's about as bad as it can get."

The door swung open and a man came in. He held up her Grammy, broken and forgotten in the brawl.

"This yours?" he asked.

Esther managed to get John Norman home and bedded down. She sat by him most of the night, fretting, puzzled. What the hell to do next? How can I snap him out of it? she wondered. What's gotten into him? Is it my success? Why should that hurt him? He's had it all, he could have it again whenever he wanted it. Besides, hadn't he pushed her toward the top for all he was worth? Despair overtook her. She knew that she loved him more than anything in the world, but she knew also, suddenly, that it might not be enough. For him and for them. She was scared now, really scared. Why couldn't she break through to him? Why did he take refuge in drink, and running away? Why couldn't he face her, talk to her about what was eating him away inside?

The next morning, the L.A. *Times* carried a front page account of the incident at the Grammies, under the headline, "Rock Star Turns Grammy Awards into Brawl." John Norman was somber, silent. Neither of them mentioned the night before, or the story in the paper. It was as though they were strangers who'd never been more than polite to each other. Esther had dismissed the cook for the day, planning to spend it alone with John Norman. But after breakfast he announced abruptly that he was going back to the ranch. He had to work on his music. He was going to make a comeback as a single, he said.

She begged him to stay. In two days, she would begin another gruelling schedule of rehearsals and tapings for her special. "I need you, Johnny," she pleaded. "Nobody knows how to direct me the way you do. You always make me give my best."

"Honey chile," he drawled, "you are already the best. The time when you needed me to make it is long gone . . . if you ever needed me."

That hurt, hurt deeply, but Esther said nothing in reply. Instead, she offered to take him to the airport. If it was what he really wanted . . . Let Mo do it, he said. They embraced for a long time, but he felt like a stranger in her arms. He's already left, she thought. He's not with me now.

When he was gone, Esther threw herself into her work. She had never done television before, and her inexperience with the medium made the work exhausting. Rehearsals seemed to drag on forever. The director considered her an upstart flash-in-the-pan and treated her accordingly. She decided that he was a pompous old fart and treated him accordingly. There were yelling scenes almost every day. Nothing seemed to go right. The situation was worsened by Esther's apparent attitude. She was short-tempered; she came on nasty, petulant; she seemed to play the big star at every opportunity. But underneath it all, she was in actuality a nervous wreck—one minute worried sick about John Norman, the next minute scared to death she'd come off on the tube looking like the plain little Jewish girl from Brooklyn she still imagined herself to be.

It got even worse when the time came for the taping. She had never before played to an empty theater. It was weird. She just couldn't come alive for those rows and rows of vacant seats. And what with the constant stopping and starting, take after take after take, she couldn't tell a damn thing about her performance. Was she good? Spectacular? Lousy? She didn't know. Her mind was torn by the anxiety about John Norman, by the fear that she couldn't pull this special off by herself.

Brian was very supportive, showing up for almost every number. He would sit well back in the darkened theater, calling encouragement to Esther between takes. Or, when she had walked off the set in frustration, he would huddle with her in the dressing room, counseling, joking, trying to cheer her up.

One afternoon they were taping "Woman in the Moon," the song she had first sung at the Indian Relief benefit, the song that had launched her career. She wanted it to be perfect; she had been arguing with the director all morning. His plan called for her to begin stage left and move across in front of a six-foot-high three-dimensional fluorescent light sculpture that spelled E-S-T-H-E-R. Then she was expected to pause, stage right, and descend a dozen carpeted steps into the orchestra, still singing. Esther insisted that the song would suffer from so much moving around. He implied that if she couldn't handle it, she was less than a pro. She became tense and angry, but she agreed to do it his way.

Esther was costumed rather starkly in full black trousers and a black satin over-blouse, cinched at the waist by a simple belt. A small, net-like cape scattered with sequins covered her shoulders. The outfit gave her an ethereal quality that was just right for the number.

The first three verses went smoothly as Esther moved across the stage. She sounded good; she truly loved this song. At the top of the stairs, launching into the fourth verse, she was thinking of John Norman:

I believe there's a best of both worlds
Mixing old and new
Recognizing change is seldom expected
As I long suspected
They believed that strange was a word for wrong

She began to descend the steps.

Well not in my song
'Cause you, you and I are changing that tune. . .

She slipped on the carpeting and stumbled, almost twisting her ankle.

"I can't sing while I'm walking downstairs," she shouted out into the theater. "I'll kill myself! That damn rug wasn't here in rehearsals! Why do they keep changing things? They don't know what they want. Oh, the hell with it . . . Somebody tell me what to do."

Brian was sprinting down the aisle toward her.

"Fucking stars!" The director's voice boomed over the P.A.

Esther stood limp, worn out. "Let's take a break," she begged an assistant director.

"Roll it back!" the voice boomed again. "Five minutes, everybody."

Brian was at her side, a reassuring arm around her shoulder. They picked their way to her dressing room through the maze of cables, equipment, technicians, chorus kids, grips, and goof-offs.

"How's it going?" he asked when they were finally alone, though he knew she was really down.

Esther began to fuss with her hair, frowning. "Fine!" she shrilled. "Lousy. I hate this show. No, I don't. I can't think about it." She threw down the comb.

"How is he?" Brian asked.

She sighed. "The same. I fly out to him on weekends. I tell him a funny story. He laughs. Only the laugh is kind of . . ." Her voice trailed off.

"A half note behind?" Brian finished her sentence.

"Yeah. And he pretends everything's all right for a day or so. And I pretend I don't notice he's pretending, and then . . ."

An assistant director stuck his head in. "Esther—" She motioned the A.D. out, and looked up at Brian, the frustration showing in her face.

"And then I can't do it any more, and I get back on the plane, lock myself in the bathroom, and scream from Tucson to L.A." Esther paused, staring at the floor. "He's been writing again, Brian. Has he talked to you about his songs?"

"No," Brian said, "he doesn't call me."

"Then why don't you call him?" She looked up irritated. "Why are you waiting to call him? You're supposed to be his oldest friend, damn it!"

"Esther?" The A.D. was back. "Can we get you to check the light in the next sequence?"

She blew her stack. "No! Not now! Can't you see we're busy?" She shoved him out and slammed the door, breathing hard.

"He is my oldest friend," Brian said. "He made me a rich man, he turned my life around." He paused. "But there's nothing more I can do for him."

How to make her understand, he thought, without coming right out and saying it, that the guy's washed up. He admired her loyalty, but knew it was blind.

"That sucks, Brian." She was angry. "There's a lot you can do for him. You can give him your time, you can give him support. You can earn your twenty-five percent and make Freddy earn her ten, and the accountants their fives and the attorney his five, and Gary his . . . I could never figure out what Gary does. Anyway, if you won't help him now, when he needs it, you're all nothing but a bunch of bloodsuckers."

"That's not justified," Brian said defensively. "I'm as good a friend as you, but I'm not in love with him. I don't have to believe something that isn't true any more." There. He'd finally spit it out.

"Don't say that, Brian!" she snapped. "He's got everything. He just needs to start using it again. I wish I could help him. I wish I could give back some of what he gave me." Sadly, she shook her head. "I look at him when he's asleep, and there's no hurt or pain in his face," she said. "Then I wish I could just wake him up so he could stay that way—calm and peaceful."

Brian said, "I remember the first time I saw him. I was peddling demos when I walked into this joint in Venice one night and there was this guy making the audience think he was bleeding. He uses himself up . . ." He paused. Didn't she comprehend the difference between herself and that reckless, violent man out there in the desert?

"You don't understand that because you don't have to do it," he told her.

"I just sing for them," she said. "Brian, his new songs are . . . different. But they're good."

"I can't protect him from himself, Esther, but I guess I could record his songs." He knew he owed that to both of them.

"You'd be doing yourself a favor, Brian." She brightened. The A.D. stuck his head in again. "Miss Hoffman, we're ready."

Esther gave Brian a big, false smile. "Radiant enough for the masses, Brian?" And she marched off to the burning lights.

That night, Brian called John Norman at the ranch and arranged to fly in the next day, "Just to shoot the shit." He made the flight in his twin-engine Gates Learjet. The plane had cost him just under $900,000, courtesy the John Norman Howard Speedway.

Brian Wexler was one of the richest, most successful managers in the business. Now he handled a small stable of superstars, but the Speedway had been the first and the biggest. They had started from scratch together.

Brian was a perfect match for John Norman. They shared an intensity and cold-eyed practicality, never wavering from the goal of more and more money. In the early days, when John Norman used to refer to himself as "just an ol' country boy," he often told Brian that he was "too L.A." That was probably the worst thing John Norman could say about anybody, since in those days he firmly believed that Los Angeles was "the worst place in the whole fuckin' world." He once told an L.A. *Times* interviewer, "There's about as much honesty in this town as there is meat in a burrito."

But he trusted Brian. By the time they got together, the band needed management badly. John Norman had been doing it all himself, mainly because he was so driven, but also because he'd never met a manager he could give a shit for. He'd heard all the horror stories from other musicians, and he knew most managers came on like Santa Claus when they were really Typhoid Mary.

On the flight to Tucson, Brian thought back over those early days. He had been as green as they come in the music business when he "discovered" the Speedway in that joint in Venice. He was still a sales rep then, but he watched, he listened, and he learned fast. He was ambitious, too, and knew he had the brains to make it. Peddling demos—demonstration records—was a good way to hear new, relatively unknown groups, and he was looking for one he could build to stardom. When he heard John Norman, he was impressed. Without approaching the band, he decided to check them out in the trade.

He found that though they had no management and no recording contract, they maintained a grueling tour schedule of over two hundred dates a year. They'd been around, and they had a legion of loyal fans in bars and clubs all over the country, particularly in the Midwest and the South. A guy Brian knew, a sometime record reviewer for *Rolling Stone*, was a real freak for the Speedway, showing up every night when they played in the L.A. area, recording them live on his own equipment.

"They've always been their own band," he told Brian. "There's just never any way you can confuse them with anybody else. Like when everybody else was into acid rock—whatever that was—with all those interminable, self-indulgent solos, the Speedway stayed away from it. They'd open in some dive with maybe a ten-minute set of thirties blues, half an hour of Jerry Lee Lewis, and then rip into their own stuff, which is far-fucking-out. Whatever they're doin', you always get the feeling that it's supposed to be fun. And it is. I'm tellin' you, man, they got a huge following out there in the boonies. And the crossover between rock freaks and hillbillies is unique. Those of us who've followed them think of them as *the* long-hair country band."

This may be just what I'm looking for, Brian had thought. After that, he listened to the band every chance he had, and finally he approached John Norman. The guy was leery, Brian remembered, but he kept pressing, buying the musicians drinks every night after the final set, talking music, emphasizing John Norman and Lee's own compositions as the best stuff they did. One night, alone with John Norman, he popped the question.

"I've checked you guys out," he said. "You got fans all over this country, but this one-night-stand routine is gonna kill you. You need a record. Those fans are sitting out there waiting to buy it. Let me get it made for you."

"You mean manage the band?" John Norman said warily.

"I mean manage the band."

John Norman scratched his beard and stared into his drink. "I figgered that's what you had in mind," he said, "so I checked you out, too. Far as I can tell, you're a two-bit peddler, a greenhorn on the make.

But I hear you're honest, which I find hard to believe about a manager. I also hear you're smart and ambitious." He paused. "So am I. I reckon we can give it a whirl."

And so Brian Wexler became part of the Speedway. He gave up every other pursuit and concentrated on them totally. Within three weeks, he had gotten them auditions with one major and two small independent labels. One of the indies bit, and though the advance was a piddling fifty thousand for a three-record deal, it was a beginning.

That first album nearly killed them all, Brian remembered. Bands have to pay their recording expenses out of their advances, and the day of the $10,000 album was long gone by then. What with first-class studio time, a good producer, and good mixing, a relatively modest album could eat up $50,000 in production costs. But by doing most of the work themselves, relentlessly beating down the cost of everything, juggling creditors, and still playing gigs almost every night, they pulled it off.

The album was a mix of fifties classics and new material written by John Norman and Lee. The band had wanted all new material, but that scared the people at the record company. They argued that the band was known for its rockabilly sound, and that was what the fans out there wanted to buy. Reluctantly, Brian had to side with the label. He did insist, however, that the label push an original as the single, a tune called "Spanish Lies."

The company was enthusiastic about the band and the album. Brian knew they'd do all they could for it. He also knew that wasn't very much. It was a small company, sloppily managed, financially marginal, and choked by the limited distribution that was the curse of its independent label. They couldn't even chip in on the tour Brian was setting up to coincide with the album's release. So he did it himself, cajoling promoters, hounding booking agents for bigger halls, longer dates, hiding from credit card companies, begging local critics in each major city to drop by and catch the band.

And despite the obstacles, it worked. Everywhere they played, the Speedway sold out. First the single, then the album began to get air play. Soon "Spanish Lies" hit the charts, rising to number seven and selling over 900,000 copies in sixteen weeks. The album did not fare as well. Though it spent thirty-three weeks on the charts, it sold fewer than 200,000 copies.

That was spectacular for a debut album, but Brian knew it was no good in relation to the single. He had learned that when you have a single hitting top ten, you should figure on selling at least one album for every three singles. That was true even of the kind of one-hit band that pads an album out with a lot of filler. You just stickered the front of the package with "Contains their big hit single, Blah-Blah," and the people who buy albums instead of singles would buy it. And he knew that with a band like Speedway, who'd been out on the road a while and had a good hippee-hillbilly crossover—giving them both AM and FM air-play—the three-to-one ratio was low. There was no excuse for the low sales figure on the album. The only way you could explain it was bad distribution. It just couldn't have been in the stores when people went to look for it. He had to break the contract. But how? He knew, as he told John Norman, "Those guys couldn't pick their noses without putting their fingers in their eye," but he also knew they were not about to let the band go.

Luck smiled on them. The label went bust and sold out to a big New York conglomerate. The new owners decided that Speedway was a country band, and they were more interested in the booming straight rock market. They balked at advancing money for a second album, claiming the band was still "in the hole" to them on the first advance. Nor would they allow the band out of the contract.

It was just the opportunity Brian had been looking for. First, he slapped them with a multimillion-dollar lawsuit charging "coercion." He knew this would scare the shit out of their lawyers, since another band, the James Gang, had just won a $600,000 court judgment in a similar case. He had kept careful records of the sloppiness of the former management, and his own lawyers were convinced he had a good case. Then he began to shop the majors for a buy-out, relentlessly pursuing A & R people, producers, marketing execs, anybody who would give him fifteen minutes. "You know the phrase 'working a building?' " one CBS Records man said. "Well, that Wexler can work a building like nobody I ever saw."

When the exhausted band came off tour, Brian proudly announced that he had two buy-out bids: CBS offered a guarantee of two years at a total advance of $420,000. Warner offered fifteen months at $300,000. He argued in favor of Warner, pointing out that they had also guaranteed $200,000 in promotion, including tour, advertising, the works. He also warned of the difficulties of doing business with CBS—an East Coast company. The band was flabbergasted, then ecstatic. They voted unanimously to accept the Warner offer.

All in all, that first year had been a good one for the John Norman Howard Speedway, as it was now called. With over $300,000 in concert bookings, plus the record company advance and publishing royalties, they grossed high numbers. Even when all their expenses had been deducted ($85,000 in salaries, $79,000 in travel expenses, $40,000 to produce the album, a whopping $66,000 in legal fees, $33,000 in office and promotional fees—including an $8000 phone bill—and a host of "miscellaneous" expenses, most of which went up their noses), their net income was $153,000, and each member of the band earned about $15,000 after taxes. The funniest thing was that after all those years of touring, the country music D.J.s voted them the "best new band" of that year. For the first time in their history, they were well known and solidly in the black. And with a new album and a new record company, the next year looked even better.

Working with Warner was like a dream come true for the band—and for Brian. He had to "work the building," of course. It was a big company, and his band was relatively unknown. He knew that getting people inside the company excited about a product was half the battle. He and the band lavished money on producing the new album, which was to be all fresh material. Meanwhile he worked closely with Warner on promotion and the tour tie-in. Most of the album was cut at the Record Plant in Marin, with Brian shuttling back and forth between L.A. and the Bay Area. John Norman was really up for this one, and his work was the best he'd ever done. He produced it himself, bringing in the best "hired guns"—studio musicians—to back up the group, driving them all to the limit of their abilities. With the help of a first-class engineer, John Norman even did the mixing himself. The sophisticated technology of recording has produced its own set of problems. The separate instrumental and vocal tracks that have been recorded at various times must be combined into a mix that has not sixteen channels, but only the two the listener will eventually hear over his stereo set. The mix on a given single chosen for release must also have a mono mix suited for radio play. The mix is as crucial as the studio work itself and is regarded in the business as an almost mystical art. John Norman worked at it for weeks. Two signs hung over his mixing console: "YOUR BASIC SOW'S EAR TO SILK PURSE CONVERTER" and "YOU CAN'T POLISH A TURD."

At last Brian and he delivered the completed master to Warner, and the great battle began over which cut should be the single release. After endless wrangling, it boiled down to two choices—a bluesy number called "I'm Able" and a solid rocker called "Watch Closely Now." The arguments dragged on and on, with John Norman and Brian favoring "Watch Closely Now," and most of the Warner brass pushing "I'm Able." Finally Brian proposed that the issue be submitted to Felix Fleischer for binding arbitration. Warner agreed.

Felix Fleischer of the Fleischer Response Studies Lab is virtually unknown beyond the inner circles of the record trade. A fine musician and an experienced psychologist, his work is based on the premise that people respond physically to music, and that these responses can be measured and recorded. Fleischer built a model based on tests on thousands of teenagers whose internal body responses he monitored while they listened to rock and roll. The model complete, he moved from measurement to prediction, claiming that he could take an unreleased record and tell with considerable accuracy whether it would be a hit. Radio stations began to use him to test the acceptability of new releases, and soon the record business beat a path to his door. As one executive put it, "The Fleischer dream machine is a little weird, but who's gonna argue with success? The guy is right a *lot* of the time." Others argued that a lot of the Fleischer "magic" was as self-fulfilling as the pure guesswork of tipsheets: word is leaked to D.J.s that Fleischer is hot on a record, so it starts getting a lot of air play. Once they hear it on the radio, the kids buy it. Shazam, it's a hit.

Fleischer did his work and the reports came back

to Burbank. The reports rated each song on a scale of one to fifty, with anything under twenty considered a bomb and a score over thirty a potential hit. "I'm Able" got a 26, "although there was a significant level of irritation in teen subjects." "Watch Closely Now" received a 37. "Experience has shown us," Fleischer wrote, "that records with a score of 28 or higher have excellent potential in terms of both sales and chart ranking. Clearly, you have a winner here." The argument was over; Warner immediately began pressing copies of "Watch Closely Now" and even decided to make it the title track.

When a rock album is released, everything happens at once. Some product can be greeted with a reaction of "What the fuck? Where did this come from?" when it arrives at a record company, but if the company is already up for the album prior to release, the sales blitz is overpowering. The business is a crap game, and the theory is that if you're betting on a winner, you do everything possible to *make* it a winner.

Brian had successfully "worked the building" and Warner geared up its powerful sales and promotion machine. A thousand copies of a press kit, together with a complimentary album, were mailed to music writers all over the country. Interviews with John Norman were set up for both *Rolling Stone* and *Country Music*. Gibson and Stromberg, at that time the most potent independent publicists in the business, were hired to promote the Speedway. A gig at the all-important Troubadour was set. This angered John Norman. He hated the Troub, hated its audience. "They don't come to hear *us*, man," he told Brian, "they come because it's the Troub. They don't think they should *like* the music; they think they should be cool and *watch* it. The house is half-comped by the record company, anyway, man. You can be blowin' shitty and they get up and shout 'Boogie!' " He told the Warner execs, "We been around, ya know? We ain't exactly a high school band." But he knew they had to do it. If you didn't play L.A., to the L.A. folks you just didn't exist.

They prepared carefully for the Troubadour opening. "We ain't givin' 'em no glitter or trash flash," John Norman said. "We're just gonna be the best goddamn band they ever heard." They were also getting up for the nationwide tour that would follow. It would climax at Max's Kansas City, in New York, the other key city for critical acceptance. At that time, Warner was putting together its now famous *Book of the Road*, a guide originally intended for its own acts, but eventually made available to everybody. It listed every conceivable piece of information a touring band might need about cities all over the world, from esoterica like the best throat doctor in Des Moines to such vital information about clubs and concert halls as the dimensions of their loading doors and the adequacy of electric power. It listed selected hotels, restaurants, musical instrument shops, record outlets, and the best local entertainment spots. It even included addresses of local VD and abortion clinics, and of the local Civil Liberties Union office.

In addition to the *Book of the Road*, Warner also supplied the group with an excellent sound system, a $50,000 package that included eight separate speakers and a mixing board with twelve outputs. By this time Bobby Ritchie had come on board, and John Norman was training him in the rigors of the road.

The day of the Troubadour opening arrived and the band was ready, but tense. They spent most of the afternoon smoking dope, watching TV, and boozing. Early in the evening, they gathered at the club for a sound check, then retired to the crummy dressing rooms to pack their noses and psych themselves up. Well-wishers dropped by with more snowy offerings. By show time, they knew they were ready to kill. At John Norman's insistence, they had secretly distributed their own free tickets to real Speedway freaks, fans from the old days. "Just as a kinda balance against the corporate assholes and Hollywood chicolas," he said.

The opening night second set, therefore, turned into a near riot, with the band stoned crazy but hot as a firecracker, and their old fans nearly wrecking the place. The next day, the Los Angeles *Times* said, "The John Norman Howard Speedway is a truly brilliant musical organization. They are also a crude and revolting bunch of drunks." Warner was a little pissed, to say the least, and Brian had a huge shouting match with John Norman. The Troubadour owner threatened to cancel the rest of the gig.

All was forgotten and forgiven two days later, however. An incredible thing happened: Station KARE, the number-one AM rock station in Los Angeles, suddenly and unexpectedly added "Watch Closely Now" to its playlist. Warner was dumbfounded; Brian and the band were jubilant. An astonishing piece of luck had come their way.

Brian was bewildered. He knew that radio stations didn't give a fuck about selling records. All they wanted to do was keep people's hands off the dials. And KARE had pioneered the hugely successful concept of the "tight playlist." In the middle sixties the station had been faltering in the ratings and a new program director had been brought in. He had promptly junked the old "Top Forty" format, which had included a playlist of sixty, allowing the D.J. to throw in a few oldies and album cuts. He also reduced D.J. chatter, shortened promo jingles, cut down on and cluttered commercials, and endlessly repeated the promo "Much More Music."

There was actually much less music. The playlist was cut from sixty to thirty-five, and the thirty-five were played in a strictly weighted order, with the top ten played more often than the bottom ten. In less than two years, KARE was number one. The message was clear: Tight playlists made money. The trend swept the country's AM stations, and it became increasingly difficult to break in new artists through air play. It got so bad that WABC in New York, the biggest and richest of them all, was rumored to have a playlist of only eighteen singles.

Warner could only figure that the new program director at KARE happened to be a freak for the Speedway and wanted to show his clout by adding the single to the playlist during its first week in release. They really didn't care why. As one grinning executive put it, "You know, we haven't really done a fucking *thing* on this one yet, but Brian Wexler's gonna be givin' us all head onstage at the Troub tonight." They all knew that just hitting the playlist meant almost immediate sales of 30,000 units, good as gold.

The next week, "Watch Closely Now" hit the charts. *Billboard* carried it at 100, *Cashbox* at 103 and *Record World* at 88 with a bullet.

The band continued the two-show-a-night grind at the Troub. Gibson and Stromberg persuaded the *Times* critic to give them another chance. This time he wrote, "Last night the John Norman Howard Speedway seemed more interested in musical credibility than in clowning around, as they had on opening night. It is a very tight, confident musical aggregation, and one to be watched carefully."

Within another week, the single was playing on KLIV in San Jose, KFRC and KSAN in San Francisco, KAKC in Tulsa, KNET in Seattle, and KWG in Portland. Then it jumped East, hitting WCUE in Cleveland, WAXY in Buffalo. FM stations started giving the album air play. The single and album both began to march up the charts, and the Warner promotion machine moved into high.

The Speedway album art featured a slightly stylized fifties stock car. T-shirts and posters were made up featuring the car. One hundred model cars almost a yard long were fabricated and used for in-store promotion. Little glass versions full of candy were sent to D.J.s.

The Speedway made its big tour, and sales and air play followed them cross-country. Promoters welcomed them with open arms and packed houses. The concert business had been in a slump, and superstars were making outrageous demands. Here was essentially a brand-new act that they already knew. As one promoter put it, "Jesus, you guys have been on the road *forever*." The Speedway was also welcome because it was a tight-knit and efficient organization. The roadies were solid professionals who did their job and didn't come on like King Shit.

Just as the Speedway opened a two-week gig in New York, the single hit number eighteen with a bullet and went on the WABC playlist. The album was soaring, too, and the Big Apple date was a sell-out. Reviews were tremendous. Both the *Stone* and the *Voice* couldn't find enough superlatives. The *New York Times* described, "exuberant, crackerjack rock, boogie and country music that had the audience in a hooting, clamoring and stomping frenzy." Everywhere, it was the same. The Boston *Phoenix*, the Baltimore *Forecast*, *Crawdaddy*, *High Fidelity*—all were favorable. Even *Variety* liked them, noting that "Speedway fans are good drinkers, which makes this act most welcome in major rock bistros."

After ten weeks on the road, the exhausted band returned to L.A. to a giant, lavish picnic on the Warner lot. Both the single and the album were number one. The single was already platinum, the album soon would be. No one doubted it. They were on their way.

There were more hit albums after that, a hugely successful world tour, television appearances—the money seemed endless. But somewhere, Brian thought as the plane touched down in Phoenix, something had gone sour. Something had snapped in John Norman's head. He had always been a loner, more than a little cold, clearly driven. But in the early days, the blatant self-destruction wasn't there. It was all work, work, work. But you could have a good time with him, too. He could jump from a discussion of the mysteries of psychokenesis to one on the mysteries of carburetors. Sure, he drank too much and doped too much, but that was the great occupational hazard of the rock racket. What had begun to scare Brian was that it became more and more difficult for John Norman to psych himself up for a performance. And he had developed a wild, crazy temper, pushing the privileges of superstardom to the limit. And beyond.

God, I dread this meeting, Brian thought as he left the jet. He knew his golden boy was finished, knew John Norman was finished because he wanted to be.

Brian paced up and down in the little house. He felt claustrophobic. John Norman was seated cross-legged on the floor, playing a guitar and singing. It was a soft, country ballad. Sad. Almost morose. He finished the song and looked up at Brian, who continued to prowl like a caged animal. John Norman knew he didn't like the music, and neither of them could think what to say.

"Didn't tell you," Brian blurted, "we had the office done over."

"Yeah?"

"No natural light gets in. Dig? Natural light means heat variation—distorts the sound. Not many people know that, ya know." He paced some more. Silence. "Got a drink?" he said. "Why don't we have a drink?"

John Norman looked at him. "I haven't had a drink before breakfast for weeks, Brian," he said, his voice deadly calm. Another long silence. Brian fiddled around the room, picking up things, putting them down.

"I like the songs," he said finally, no enthusiasm in his voice.

"I know you do," John Norman said, "but you can't do anything with 'em." His voice turned bitter. "Don't bullshit me, Brian. We know each other too long."

"Well," Brian said carefully, "you got yourself a very different sound there, John Norman . . . different sound altogether." He paced, his face grim. "I don't think they'll buy what they don't know. We'll give 'em some of your golden oldies, the shit that made you a household word." He became enthusiastic. "I'll fix it. No favors. I'll make a mint!"

"Fact is," John Norman said slowly, "I didn't know what to say when you came out here, Brian. You're my oldest friend, so I couldn't say 'no, you can't have my songs. Fact is, I figure on producing 'em myself."

Brian leaped at the out. "Oh, that's great!"

"And publishing—why the hell split the publishing? I can do it all myself." John Norman flashed an unpleasant smile. "I want to be a mogul like you."

"Fantastic," Brian said. "It's time you got into it." The guy's really gone, he thought.

They didn't talk much after that. Brian brought news of Esther—her successful special, her new album, the growing press coverage. John Norman seemed uninterested. He volunteered to drive Brian back to Tucson. They had spent less than two hours together.

On the runway next to the sleek jet, John Norman pulled the jeep to a stop. It was an awkward moment for both of them.

"So," Brian said.

"Yeah." John Norman smiled weakly. "Stay low, keep movin', stay away from women with worse troubles than your own . . ." His voice trailed off.

Brian got out of the jeep. "I wish I could help," he said.

"Yeah," John Norman said, "I wish you could, too."

Brian stood for a moment, feeling as shitty as he ever had in his life. Then he turned and sprinted to the plane.

Chapter XIII

The dogs ran out and surrounded the jeep, yapping loudly. Mo came waddling out from the back of the big house. He seemed surprised to see John Norman, who climbed wearily out of the jeep, dusty and tired to the bone. He had just driven five hundred miles in ten, twelve hours . . . he himself had no clear idea of how long he'd been on the road. All he knew was that he was so exhausted he could hardly stand up. All he wanted was a bottle, a bath, and a bed, in that order.

"Esther didn't say you was comin'," said Mo, looking puzzled. "She'll be home about six," he called after John Norman, who brushed by him without a word and went into the house.

The front hall was empty, and there was a feeling of disuse about the place, as though nobody had lived there for a very long time. And there was dust, which surprised John Norman, because Esther was so meticulous. He wandered into the enormous living room. It, too, was empty, although a faint sound of music, as if from a radio, came from somewhere in the distance. On a tabletop, with his forefinger, John Norman slowly spelled out the word D-U-S-T.

The telephone rang, but he paid no attention to it,

and soon it stopped ringing. As he trailed his way through the house, the sound of the radio grew louder until it intruded on his thoughts. Curious, he went looking for it.

It was coming from the swimming pool. As John Norman pushed open the French doors that led to the pool area, he could see a girl swimming in the pool. John Norman didn't recognize her.

"Who are you?" he called out.

The girl swam over to the edge of the pool and bobbed up, brushing wisps of long hair off her face. She was a skinny little waif with big eyes. "Quentin," she answered. "Remember, I used to be with Gary Danziger?"

"Oh, that Quentin," said John Norman. He didn't remember, but it figured. This kid looked about fifteen, and none of Danziger's cast of thousands was above the legal limit. "It was a Tuesday or some such. . ."

His irony was lost on the girl, whose education had never stretched to irony. She scrambled nimbly out of the pool, like a small animal. She was wearing jeans shorts and nothing else; her breasts were surprising on so tiny a girl. Taking up a T-shirt from a nearby table, she began to pull it over her head.

"How did you get in?" John Norman wanted to know.

"I came in with the pool man," said Quentin, her voice muffled by the shirt. She tugged it down over her shorts. It was a JOHN NORMAN HOWARD SPEEDWAY shirt. "Guess how long I've had this?"

"Since you were with Gary Danziger," said John Norman, turning to go. He had no eyes for this damp chick or her inane babbling; all he wanted was a drink and to sleep. He'd even skip the bath for now.

"I was with him for a week." The girl was tagging along behind him; it was obvious that she wouldn't be shaken easily. She wasn't even aware that she was intruding.

"Oh, it was a meaningful relationship," said John Norman dryly.

Still dripping, Quentin followed him indoors, her clogs squishing wetly on the polished living room floor.

"Hey, listen, you can help me out," she said.

"You can help *me* out by leaving," said John Norman, pouring himself a drink.

But Quentin wasn't paying attention. She was walking around the room, checking out the household goods of a rock-and-roll star.

"Hey, listen," she chattered loudly, "I'd like an interview. I string for *Rolling Stone* now, and all the pop magazines. I'd like an *exclusive* interview."

"Sure you would," said John Norman sarcastically.

He'd been down this road before. These chickies were all the same, they all wanted to ball a big name. They didn't care whose body was attached to the name, as long as they could tell their friends that they'd been to bed with Mick This or David That. The way this groupie chick was touching the guitars, the console, and the other instruments was almost lewd. It was as though she were getting off on the equipment and the money it represented. John Norman turned away. He really didn't want to look at her.

"Hey, listen!" Quentin was babbling. "This is out of sight! Terr-if-ic! It blows the mind!"

Mind? What mind? thought John Norman. "You have a real way with words," he told her. "I can't wait to see what you write."

Once again, his meaning went over the girl's head. She came toward him, wiggling her ass in what she thought was a seductive walk. Actually, it made her look as though she had crabs.

"Listen," she said huskily, dropping her eyes. "I'd do anything for this interview. You can ask Gary what I'd do."

"And I'm sure he'd tell me." John Norman wasn't interested.

"Gary says I'm terrific. He really gets off on me."

This blatant come-on was too much for John Norman. This stoned-out, brainless groupie, with her lack of allure, her lack of honesty and womanliness, was everything he had come to hate. His head began to ache, and he wished that either he or she were a thousand miles from here.

"Gary's been known to say that," he said without interest. What streak of masochism kept him standing here, talking to this idiot? Why didn't he just throw her out?

"Do me the favor?" The girl was still halfway across the room from John Norman, but she was getting ready to come real close.

"Because you're terrific?"

"I'd like this interview," she begged, looking as flirtatious as she could. Then she giggled, a repulsive sound.

"Terrific," said John Norman flatly.

"Exclusive," she stressed, arching significantly.

"Out of sight," said John Norman.

Quentin giggled again. "With Esther."

Something red and hating exploded inside John Norman.

The Cadillac pulled through the gates and wound around the driveway to the front door. An exhausted Esther got out, but when she saw the jeep standing there, a brilliant smile lighted up her face. He was back! He was home!

"John Norman, you're back!" she called as she ran into the living room. Music was blaring from the huge speakers, but the room was empty. But he's here! I know he's here! God, how she needed him right now! This was the best thing that had happened to her this week! This month!

Shouting his name over and over, Esther ran up the stairs. He must be in the bedroom. Or maybe taking a shower. There was a dim light coming from under the bedroom door. He was there. Flinging open the door, Esther ran into their bedroom.

"John Norman, I . . ." she broke off, aghast.

John Norman was in bed all right, but he wasn't alone. There was a girl lying underneath him, a skinny girl, vaguely familiar to Esther. John Norman was holding her down, apparently by force, because she was squealing and breathing hard, even though she was chewing gum.

Esther stood wordless, watching John Norman and the girl disentangle themselves. God, he looks ridiculous! flashed through Esther's mind. Nothing looks more foolish than a man caught with his weenie out! She almost laughed, but fought to control the hysteria.

It was only a moment that passed, but to Esther it seemed like a year, a year of appalled silence, of humiliation, of a rising, burning anger that filled her, blocked all else out.

John Norman rolled off the girl and looked up at his wife. He blinked slowly several times, as if unsure who it really was.

"She wants an interview with you," he slurred.

At once, Quentin came to life. "Yeah. Far out," she chirped, hopping out of bed. "I'll get my tape recorder . . ."

She started to pull on her clothes.

But Esther still stood speechless, unmoving, her eyes fixed on John Norman and the little tramp. Even dimwit Quentin could see that something wasn't right.

"What's wrong with her?" she asked John Norman. "Is she gonna talk to me or what?" She tugged at his arm. "I tried, I really did . . . but . . ." she pleaded. Ignoring her, he stared blankly at Esther.

"You dirty son of a bitch!" Esther exploded suddenly, her face going white.

The light dawned suddenly on Quentin. Esther was upset! She was jealous! What a gas! Far freaking out! Morality, man! That was from the fifties! She laughed.

John Norman turned to look at the girl for the first time since Esther had walked in. "Get out," he told her. "Get out."

"Hey, it's okay," protested the groupie. To Esther, she said, "He couldn't make it, anyway."

"Put it in the interview!" Esther roared. "Don't leave anything out!" She turned to John Norman, who was now struggling to get his jeans on, and took one step forward.

"Get out!" He rushed at Quentin, giving her a little push.

"I've had it with you!" stormed Esther. "You can trash *your* life, but you're not going to trash mine!" Angry tears blinding her eyes, she ran out of the bedroom. Half-formed thoughts swirled in her head, but she wasn't capable of putting them together. All she could do was run, run . . . and then strike out, smashing, breaking, destroying.

John Norman ran after her. He saw Esther halfway down the hall, picking up a large planter that held a rare fern. Before he could speak, she had thrown it to the floor, breaking the pot into a hundred pieces. Now she ran to the head of the stairs, where she pulled a painting down from the wall and hurled it away from her as though it were an enemy.

John Norman chased her down the stairs, grabbing for her. But she shook him off and kept on running, almost falling. He sensed that she had no idea of where she was running to, or what she was running from. She had to keep moving; it was a feeling that John Norman recognized. He could see her pain, and it tore at him, because he'd caused it, because he would always cause it, as long as they were together.

Running from him like a wounded wild animal, with great, guttural sobs coming from deep within her chest, Esther reached for anything in her path that she could break or tear or smash. Her pain could be alleviated only by passing along the destruction that ripped at her soul. She did it instinctively, like a cat clawing at its tormentor. But something kept her away from John Norman, so that she wouldn't tear him into pieces with a maenad's fury.

John Norman could hear the sound of breaking glass ahead of him as he followed her from room to room. "Esther! For God's sake!" he yelled, anguished. He didn't even notice Quentin dashing past him as she ran for the front door and safety.

There was broken glass everywhere, and he picked a piece of it up in his foot. It bit into his flesh as Esther's weeping bit into his heart. Limping, his foot bleeding, he caught up with her in the old game room where she was dashing their beautiful cut-crystal decanter to the floor.

"Leave me alone!" she shrieked. "Don't touch me!"

"For God's sake, Esther, you're going to hurt yourself!" He reached for her, trying to pinion her arms, wanting to hold her until her rage and misery were spent. He had never seen her like this, never imagined her capable of such fury. She struggled in his arms, as strong and agile as a mountain cat. Twisting and turning so that he could not keep his grip on her, she began to beat at him with her small fists, the deep, wrenching sob-moans still coming from her.

At first he defended himself, and when Esther picked up a cue from the pool table and struck out at him with it, he tried to wrest it from her hands. Then, after a minute, he gave up resistance and stood meekly, his hands hanging at his sides, allowing her to beat him.

"Fight, you bastard!" Esther taunted through gritted teeth. "Protect yourself! I'm going to kill you!"

Blind with rage, she raised the heavy cue, ready to smash it down on his head. He grabbed for the thin end of the stick, and it snapped in his hand as she tried to pull it back. The stump flew up and struck her face. A red welt formed instantly on her cheek.

"Now, by God, quit it!" cried John Norman. He

reached for her again, hoping to calm her, but Esther screamed like a soul in torment. "I'll kill you! I'll kill you! I'll kill you! I'll kill you!" Her fists beat at his face, his chest, his arms.

And then, suddenly, exhaustion overtook her and she slumped in his arms, totally drained. The violence was spent; she had nothing left—no anger, no grief, nothing but a sense of total emptiness, of loss. Heaving for breath, she crumpled like a paper doll, and he laid her gently down on the couch. He looked anxiously into her face.

"That girl . . ." he said tentatively. "It didn't mean anything . . ."

"Don't insult me!" cried Esther. "She doesn't have anything to do with it!" Oh, why couldn't he understand? Why didn't he realize that she was trying to reach him, to break through to him? Words couldn't do it; he didn't understand actions, either. Why wouldn't he let her reach him? Why did he keep that essential piece of himself hidden from her and the rest of the world?

John Norman bent over her. In a whisper that was barely audible, he said, "I tried to teach you, babe . . . I tried to tell you. It's no good with me."

Esther's blue eyes blazed with renewed fury. "You never had anything to teach me, you dumb bastard. It was good! It *was* good! You stupid ass!"

"Esther, listen to me." He tried to speak, but she wouldn't let him. "Shut up!" she cried fiercely. "What are you trying to do, make me hate you so I'll let you go? Oh, how corny!"

"Please, Esther . . ." he began.

"Shut up! Don't try to say anything!" Recoiling, she turned her face away, and her voice dropped from a shout to a whimper. She seemed suddenly very young and very vulnerable, like a little girl. "I don't like you any more," she said plaintively. "I feel like killing you. And I don't like me any more, either. 'Cause I wanted you, and you're a piece of shit!"

It was more than John Norman could take. He turned to go.

"Don't you turn your back on me, you fucking coward!" Esther shrieked.

"Aw, hell," he said helplessly, "I don't want to do this to you any more." He didn't know how to deal with her. She wanted something from him, but he didn't know what it was, or how to give it to her. It would be better for both of them if he split.

"Well, then fight for me, goddamn it! Because if you keep walking, I'm going to hate you . . ." She glared at him as he turned back to her slowly. ". . . and I'll hate you forever, you son of a bitch!"

Esther began to cry, but held her head high and glared at him angrily.

John Norman came back to her, his arms out. She tried to avoid him, but he pulled her soft body to him and held her tight.

"I love you, Esther," he said softly into her neck. He'd said it out loud, he thought. Would bad luck follow?

"I hate you," she sobbed.

He whispered into her ear, "I love you."

"I hate you," she breathed back, and bit his neck so hard that he jerked his head away in pain.

"I love you," he said, pinning her wrists with one strong hand, holding her so that she couldn't bite him again.

Silently, they wrestled with each other, each of them exerting full strength. Why were they doing battle, struggling with their bodies? Was it because they were trying to match their souls, to contend with each other's spirit, to battle for the joining of their beings?

"I love you," he said.

"I love you," she said.

She was wearing a Chinese silk jacket over her rehearsal clothes, and he pulled it off her slowly, glorying in the silken feel of the fabric, the silken feel of her flesh. Esther's hair shone like a helmet of ancient bronze as she lay back on the oriental carpet, watching John Norman as he pulled his jeans off his lean body.

And then he was with her, on her, in her, and it had never been so good, so fulfilling. Even in the days when they had first become lovers, those days and nights when they'd spent long hours exploring each other's secret places, it had never been so good as it was now. Ah, she thought, don't let this end! Please, let time freeze now, at this very moment. When will we ever have this, just this again? Esther looked up at his face, at the shadowed lids of his eyes, closed in ecstasy, at the love-twisted mouth, at the straining cords of his neck. I love him so much, she thought. Is this the only way I will ever be able to reach him? As she felt the urgency building up inside her, as the moment of climax rushed to overtake her, she cried out, "Oh, God! If I could only make you feel the way you make me feel!"

But John Norman didn't hear her.

They went back to the ranch, of course. It was the only place they could be free together, without the world trying to change things for them. They would ride, and go to sleep early, look at the stars; they would make love every hour of the day in every corner of the house.

"Oh, joy," crowed Esther one evening as they sat before a cheerful fire. "No phones!"

John Norman gave her a sidelong glance. Was this the girl who had once told him, "I just happen to love it when the phone rings?"

"Did you call Brian about the tour?" Esther was bubbling with happiness; she had finally gotten John Norman to agree that he would tour with her. Mr. and Mrs.

"No," said John Norman. "I'll go into town . . .

maybe tomorrow." He avoided her happy face; he had never told her about the little talk that he and Brian had once had about a joint tour. He knew that nothing had really changed since then, except that Esther had become an even bigger star.

"Daddy, tell me a story," chirped Esther. "Tell me about the road . . . I want to hear about the road."

John Norman smiled at his wife. He loved to see her like this, so spontaneously happy, so filled with enthusiasm. Deepening his voice to his best good ol' boy timbre, he told her about the road.

"You got your hamburger, you got your double burger, you got your hamburger platter . . ." He recited the familiar litany. "You got your high-rise Holiday Inn, you got your low-rise Holiday Inn, you got your limo, you got your driver. You got your fluorescent tan. The Magic Fingers I don't need . . . I got yours."

"I want fresh curd cheese and a light white wine in the dressing room," Esther demanded. "I want you on top in the billing."

"We alternate billing. Separate . . . but equal," he said with mock solemnity.

"And every fifth day off."

"Remember her when she was just another girl waiting for the phone to ring?" John Norman asked the empty air. "Now she wants white wine and every fifth day off."

"Everything," agreed Esther with a delighted grin. "I want it all. You. Music. The screaming crowds. Cats. Dogs. Babies. Everything people have."

She looked at John Norman, searching his face for answers. "Everything's going to be all right, isn't it?" she asked softly.

"You know what you said the other night?" he said slowly.

Something in his tone made Esther nervous. She shivered a little. "I don't want to talk. I'm tired of words . . . they don't do any good."

"About how you weren't going to let me trash your life?" John Norman persisted.

She wanted desperately to evade the turn this conversation was taking. "I don't even know what I said," she told him, scared. "I don't even remember."

"Yeah, well, I do." He thought for a moment. "I liked what you said. You were right."

Esther stared into the flames that glowed from the fireplace. "Yes, well, maybe I can teach you something, too."

Picking up his guitar, John Norman struck a few chords, then worked out a tune. "I liked it because it sounded like you knew who you were."

Esther's chin came up, and she looked him straight in the eye. "I am Esther Hoffman Howard," she announced.

"Yeah. And don't ever forget it."

"You got any more instructions, teach?"

"Yeah. I want you to lay off the chocolate," he told her gruffly. "Also, I love you."

John Norman grinned, and he looked so boyishly handsome that Esther felt a warmth growing within her. "Take me to bed before I change your billing," she said.

So he did.

They made love all night, first with a passion that rose almost to jungle heights, and later with great tenderness—slowly, savoring each kiss and movement. It was after four in the morning when Esther fell asleep, but an hour later she woke again. She woke at the sound of John Norman moving around the bedroom.

Esther opened one eye reluctantly. John Norman was pulling on his pants, tucking in his plaid wool shirt. He moved quietly, hoping not to disturb her, but she was always a light sleeper—even the lightest footfall entered her dreams.

"Where are you going?" The words came out fuzzily.

John Norman bent to kiss her. "Town," he whispered. "I'm gonna call Brian." Taking his fringed buckskin jacket from the closet, he threw it on, then picked up his boots. "You want to come?" he asked.

Esther stretched sleepily, like a cat, then burrowed cozily down into the blankets. "Uh-huh," she yawned. "Just give me a second to get myself together here . . ."

"No," said John Norman, touching her shoulder. "No, don't get up. I'll talk to him."

He walked to the stairs of the loft bedroom, but lingered there, watching Esther almost hungrily.

"What?" she asked sleepily.

"Just looking."

She was three-quarters asleep again now, and going down, down, down into a dream. The room was cold with the early morning desert frost. John Norman pulled off his heavy leather jacket and carried it to the side of the bed, laying it over Esther's shoulders. It would keep her warmer than anything else, he thought. He touched her again, not taking his eyes off her. On the shoulder, on the face. She didn't wake up, although she stirred slightly.

Esther, he thought. Esther, I love you. You're great . . . a great singer, a great star, a great woman. I owe you a lot. And I'm going to find a way to pay you back. Because you deserve it. You deserve better than me. You're good, Esther, and you worked hard to make me good. But it's too late for me to be good, baby. I've been bad too long. I'm set in my ways, and they're bad ways.

He remembered suddenly the first night he saw her, back at that little club. You're blowing my act, she'd told him. You were right, Esther. I have been blowing your act. My act, too. I'm gonna try to shape up, he thought. Somehow. But I'll never be good. Not in the way you want and need, baby. Not in the way you deserve. He touched her one more time, gently,

gently on the cheek. Then he turned and left the loft bedroom.

John Norman tiptoed carefully down the stairs, carrying his boots in one hand. Setting them by the door, he moved noiselessly into the kitchen and grabbed a six-pack of Coors from the fridge. He tucked it under one arm and padded back toward the front of the house, pausing in the living room. He stood for a moment, then made a slow three-hundred-and-sixty-degree turn, looking carefully over the little house. His gaze held at the loft bedroom for a long time. Then, as if he had come to some conclusion, he strode purposefully toward the door, swooping up his boots on the way out.

It was cold outside. Goddamn cold and damp, as only the early morning desert can be. He shivered in the thin wool shirt. Sitting down in the dusty front yard, he popped a can of beer and began pulling on his boots. The light was the peculiar, clear, pale blue-gray of the American Southwest.

Slowly, he sipped a beer and contemplated the fire-engine red Ferrari that sat not ten yards away. God, how he loved that little fucker! It was one of the few material possessions he really cared about, and one of the few he took care of. He remembered the day he bought it. The band had just renewed their contract with Warner, and he, Brian, and the boys had gone on a midday tear. They ended up cruising the used car lots on Sunset—those places that specialize in custom-built jobbies that some fading star had ordered but couldn't pay for. They'd been stoned and silly, kicking the tires of a lot of big Caddies and, Rolls-Royces, acting like a bunch of hicks. None of them had any intention of buying anything.

But then John Norman had spotted the little Ferrari and fallen in love with it. It had obviously been custom-built to racing specifications; there was no imaginable option it did not have. "How much?"

he asked the dude. "Twenty-two five," the man said. "Sold!" John Norman whooped. He drove the pretty little thing right out of the lot, leaving Brian to worry about paying for it. Yes, sir, he thought, me and that car seen some good times together.

He drained the beer and popped another, moving toward the little car. Slowly he walked around it, admiring the graceful lines. It was a car built for speed and nothing else. He climbed in and started the engine, pulling the choke all the way out against the cold and damp. To him, it was like a musical instrument: it had to be perfectly tuned or it just didn't play well. Once he had it properly warmed up, he climbed out and opened the hood, listening intently to the revving engine as a doctor might hover over a patient. He detected a faint ping and adjusted the carburetor slightly. If you weren't careful, these high-speed mothers could throw a rod at eighty miles an hour and it was all over.

Satisfied, he settled down behind the wheel, popped open his third beer, and pulled away from the house toward the highway. As he hit the first two-lane blacktop, he slipped an old Speedway cassette into the tape deck. It was him singing "Watch Closely Now" from their "Greatest Hits" album. Jesus, he thought, that was a long time ago.

He headed for the freeway, turning south when he got there, toward Douglas and the Mexican border. He felt good in the speeding car, on his own, the way he liked to be. The machine felt good under him, too, moving him almost soundlessly across the barren landscape at a steady seventy-five miles an hour. There was a special kind of high you got from driving alone in a truly great automobile, especially at this special time of day on a deserted highway.

As he zoomed under the big green-and-white sign that read DOUGLAS 6 MILES, he increased his speed to ninety, pressing the accelerator only slightly and thrilling to the instant response. He could feel it between his legs. It was as if the car lifted slightly off the ground. He sensed the heat and vibration from the Ferrari creeping up his tailbone. The wind roared around his head.

On and on John Norman drove, relishing that special feeling of moving fast and being no place. He was doing a good hundred miles an hour now, but it wasn't enough. He slammed another cassette into the deck, turning the volume way up so he could hear it over the whipping wind. It was Esther singing her biggest hit, "Lost Inside of You." As always, her voice sent a thrill right through him. He threw back his head and laughed out loud—a long, deep-felt laugh of pure freedom.

Pressing the accelerator to the floor, John Norman forced the speeding Ferrari to its limits. The speedometer hit a hundred and forty; he reached down and turned the volume all the way up.

Chapter XIV

The Arizona State Police had arranged to meet Brian at the Tucson airport with a Highway Patrol helicopter. It was Brian's name and telephone number that John Norman carried in his wallet on the "In Case of Emergency" card. His only identification was his California driver's license and an Arco gas credit card.

When the telephone call came, Brian's first thought was: here it is at last. I knew it would happen some day, and here it is. His second thought was of Esther. Did she know? There was no telephone at the ranch—had the police told her yet?

"No, sir, did this Howard fella live in Arizona? He had no Arizona identification on him."

Don't tell her, Brian ordered. He arranged to fly out of L.A. in his private plane, to meet the police at Tucson. We'll pick her up by helicopter, he said. I'll tell her myself. He dreaded it, dreaded the nightmare of seeing John Howard mangled, of watching Esther see him too.

But the police had done their work well. By the time the helicopter touched down at the accident site, John Norman's body lay on the ground ten feet away from the totaled car, covered with a rough wool blanket. His face was unmarred, and strangely peaceful, except for some blood.

He's sleeping, thought Esther, as she ran toward him. He's sleeping, or he's joking. Damn him, he's always joking about death! It's not funny, John Norman. Get up, Johnny!

Off the side of the road, the red Ferrari lay smashed beyond recognition, a tangled, tortured mass of scrap metal. Highway patrol cars, an ambulance, and fire engines ringed it, and two-way radios were squawking. Photographers were snapping pictures; when they saw Esther getting out of the helicopter, they crowded forward, clicking their shutters.

Brian tried to keep her away from the body, but Esther fought past him. They're always trying to keep me from Johnny, she thought. She remembered that first concert at the raceway. Where he rode that big Harley and crashed it. They didn't want me near him then, either. Ah, John Norman, why did fast wheels fascinate you so? Why couldn't you stay on the ground where it's safe? Stay with me where it's safe and warm? She walked very slowly toward the body, slowly, steadily, never taking her eyes from his peaceful, blood-flecked face.

The sun was up, but Esther shivered in the heavy jacket she wore, John Norman's fringed buckskin jacket. When she reached his side, she stood very still for what seemed to Brian a long, long time; then she sank slowly to her knees. With loving hands, she began to smooth John Norman's clothes, brushing dust off his jacket, straightening his shirt collar. With a corner of her skirt, she began to clean the blood off his face. Poor Johnny, she thought, your face is dirty. Are you cold, baby? You look cold.

"He needs another blanket," she called over her shoulder, her eyes still on his face. "Could you bring another blanket, please? Shhhhh." She didn't want all those men to disturb John Norman, all those noisy men moving behind her, looking at her and Johnny.

She took John Norman's hands in hers, feeling them, massaging the fingers to restore the circulation. His hands were so cold, poor darling, so cold. "Okay, it's okay," she murmured over and over, stroking and patting him, rubbing his arms and feeling for his temperature. "It's okay," she whispered, touching his shoulder. "It's gonna be okay."

It was more than Brian Wexler could stand. "Esther . . ." he began, approaching her.

"I need to be quiet, please," said Esther softly. "Would you please tell them to go away? Please ask them to stop looking at him." She did not turn to Brian as she spoke, did not take her eyes from John Norman's face. Brian backed away, stricken.

Esther's hands moved to John Norman's face. With infinite gentleness she felt his forehead, as though he were a child with a fever. Pushing his hair back, she smoothed it along his high brow, then touched his bearded cheek. She could fix it, she was sure. She could make it better. Didn't I always make it better for you, John Norman?

"I'm scared, Johnny." She leaned forward to whisper directly into his ear. "I want you to hold me . . ."

But he couldn't hold her, so she cradled him instead, putting her arms tightly around him and rocking back and forth, humming to him. It was the first song they had ever worked on together, "Lost Inside of You," the song he had put words to that first morning in her little bungalow apartment. She knew he loved to hear her sing it, and she sang it to him now, rocking him in her arms, making it all better.

"They've got to move him, Esther," said Brian gently, bending to help her up.

"What?" She had no idea of what was going on, but she allowed Brian to help her stand. Bewildered, disoriented, she looked around her. The stretcher men were approaching.

"C'mon, honey," said Brian, tugging at her arm.

She could not go. She watched anxiously as John Norman's body was placed on the stretcher, and when they carried him to the waiting ambulance, she followed at his side.

"Please be gentle with him. He doesn't like to be pushed around. You know? Be careful now, don't hurt him." Her hand touched his covered body, stroked it.

As the stretcher bearers slid the body into the back of the ambulance, she eluded Brian's grasp and slipped into the vehicle with John Norman.

"Esther. It will be all right. You'll see," promised Brian.

For the first time since the helicopter had landed, she looked directly at Brian Wexler. "It'll never be all right," she said, as the ambulance doors closed on her and her man.

They took John Norman Howard back to Los Angeles for burial; Esther was afraid he'd be lonely at the ranch. It was a large funeral, attended by many celebrities and all the press, and Esther walked through it like a well-mannered robot. She wore black, and it made her shiver when she walked past a mirror. John Norman had always hated her in black.

There was speculation in the papers and magazines about just how John Norman had died. Had he O.D.'d at the wheel? Had a heart attack? Been so drunk that he went off the road? Had an accident? Committed suicide? The theories were endless, and soon a cult began to form around him. It was always that way; it had been the same with Joplin, and Morrison, with Hendrix and Duane Allman and Richard Fariña. Esther didn't read a word of it, or contribute to any part of it. She kept John Norman private. She'd always wanted him private. Just the two of them, alone and together.

She discovered that she couldn't stay in the big

house on Angelo Drive. The only things that she had ever liked about it were John Norman and the water-bed. One was gone and the other empty. Everybody agreed that it would be good for her to get out of the big house, and Freddy had found her a small, comfortable place in Laurel Canyon.

It took her a long time to pack, even though she wasn't taking much with her. It was just that she seemed to get tired easily these days; there seemed to be so much to do. Also, much as she wished to leave the house, there were traces and memories of John Norman everywhere in it, and they were hard to break away from.

On the last day in the big house, Esther sat alone in the living room, in the rocking chair she and John Norman had loved so much. She remembered how they'd found it in Pasadena, at the giant flea market there. As soon as she'd laid eyes on it, she'd known that she had to own it. It was almost exactly like the one her grandmother used to have. They'd bargained for it, laughing and joking, finally getting it at a good price. All the way home in the van, Esther had kept one hand on the chair while she told John Norman story after story about her grandmother—*bubba* they'd called her—and how *bubba* would sing Yiddish songs to her little Esther, holding the child on her lap in the big old rocker. John Norman had been fascinated, and when they'd got home, he'd carried the rocker into the house, installed Esther in it, and demanded Yiddish songs.

"Next you'll be asking for chopped liver and *kreplach*!" Esther had hooted.

"What's a kreplach?" John Norman had asked innocently, sending her into a fit of laughter.

But she had sung to him. She'd sung *Aufen Pripichuk* and the song about the greenhorn cousin and half a dozen more, while he sat on the rug, grinning up at her, not understanding a word. How clear that memory was!

Around her now, men from the moving company were packing crates and shifting cartons, but she neither saw nor heard them. She was alone with John Norman.

Where had she failed him? Was it because she'd wanted to get married; had she clipped his wings? No, that wasn't it. Why could she never communicate with him? Why couldn't they understand each other, when they'd loved each other so very much? She was sure of that; you don't mistake that. If she'd been different, a different girl . . . no, that wasn't it. John Norman had had dozens of different girls, and they hadn't helped him. It had been Esther he'd wanted, Esther he'd married.

What if she'd come along a couple of years earlier? Would he have been saved? It was a foolish question . . . they'd met when they'd met; it was their karma.

Was it John Norman's karma to die when he had? She heard Brian's voice again. He's used himself up, Brian had said, he's used himself up. If she could only deny that! But she knew that the truth about John Norman lay there, if anywhere. He was a man who had been afraid to express his doubts and fears, afraid to communicate fully with any other human being, even the woman he'd been in love with, and so he ran away. Booze, pills, cocaine, fast motorcycles and cars . . . he ran at top speed, using all of them. And in doing so he'd used himself up.

But he *had* loved her; they *had* been through so many happy times together. Was there anything she could have done differently? Should have done differently? She'd never know. But she didn't think so. I couldn't reach him because nobody could reach him. But sometimes I did. And those were the times when we were both so happy. And those were the times he never had with anybody else. That made her feel a little better.

John Norman shouted, "Pick it up out there in the

kitchen! Ah, no. Goddamn it! Hello? Who do you want? She's not here!"

It was John Norman's voice; there was no doubt about it. It was John Norman's voice!

Esther flung herself out of the rocking chair, her face pale. "John! John Norman!" she called. Somewhere in the house she could hear him singing, could hear him improvising a tune on the guitar. Suddenly the phone rang again, and she heard his voice answering it.

"I'll tell Miss Hoffman. For sure. No, I won't forget . . ."

He was here! Alive, and in this house! Running from room to room, Esther searched for the voice.

The rooms were empty, and her footsteps echoed through them as she ran. She could still hear him singing, humming, making a song up. Oh, where was he? Why couldn't she find him? This damn house was so big!

At the door of John Norman's recording room, she paused, out of breath. A pair of moving men were packing the complex equipment, and one of them turned to her.

"Lady? How do you turn this thing off?" he asked, pointing to the cassette player from which John Norman's voice still came. A cassette tape. It wasn't Johnny, it was a tape. A goddamn tape.

Esther moved into the room and pressed a button. Instantly, the voice stopped and the cassette popped into her hand. Clutching it, she carried it into the vast, empty ballroom, the largest room in the whole empty house. It was the room she'd skated in that first day here. Now it was dark and dead.

She stood in the center of the floor, the tape of John Norman held so tightly that her fingers ached. The feelings that she had been holding back for days welled up suddenly, and she could no longer contain them. They spilled out like bile, bitter and choking,

"What the hell is wrong with you?" she shrieked into the void of the room. "Why did you do this? You son of a bitch! You don't know how to live!" she screamed at John Norman. "You don't know how to keep promises! You don't know anything, you don't feel anything! You're dead! You fucking coward, you big shit! I'm gonna live forever, fucker! Liar! You lied to me!"

She broke down, sobbing deep, gasping sobs of mingled rage and grief. Then she smashed the cassette, pulling out the tape and hurling it from her, yard after yard of it. Finally, exhausted, she bent and scooped it up. The tape spilled through her fingers, useless now. Useless and dead. As dead as John Norman Howard.

"Oh, God!" wept Esther, but more quietly now. "Oh, I hate this! I hate it!" Almost calmly, she spoke again to John Norman.

"Okay." Her mouth trembled, but she blinked the tears from her eyes, and squared her shoulders. "There were so many things I wanted to tell you," she said quietly. "So many things. But we never had the time."

A dead rock star is a love object. A new poster went up on Sunset, featuring John Norman at his best and most beautiful. It advertised the album that had been re-pressed and rushed into the stores. It was an anthology, "The Best of. . . ." and it was selling like gangbusters. Bebe Jesus scheduled a twenty-four-hour eulogy that consisted of interviews with John Norman's more famous friends interspersed with cuts from the new album. Esther refused to appear on the program. Her memory was longer than the disc jockey's.

Mike Belkin, the promoter, scheduled a memorial concert and sold twenty-one thousand seats overnight. Brian, attached as usual to the telephone, refused

Belkin's demand for Esther. They were at her house; she had just come out of the pool.

"I don't give a shit you sold twenty-one thousand seats!" Brian barked into the instrument. "She's not going on." Nodding at Esther, who picked up a towel and began drying her hair, he continued. "Mike, it's okay, the boys want to do this, and we appreciate their feeling. But you can't ask her to . . ."

"I'm going on," said Esther.

It was a great concert, one of the memorable musical occasions that become a yardstick for all that follow, like Woodstock or Monterey Pop or Bangla Desh. Celebrated performers who didn't have a word to say to John Norman during the last years of his life now came forward to talk about how they loved him, and to play their music. It was star turn after star turn, a love feast. The audience ate it up and begged for more. Dry-eyed, Esther watched the evening from backstage. She was going on last. His widow. Because she was the one the curious had come to see.

"Need anything, babe?" asked Brian, poking his head into her dressing room. She was adding the finishing touches to her outfit, getting ready to go onstage.

"No."

Bobby Ritchie sprinted in. "You're on!"

Taking a deep breath, Esther stood up and started out. She paused before a box of white roses on a table by the door. White roses. The night she had become a star, the night of the Indian benefit concert, John Norman had handed her a white rose. Now she selected one for herself, and held it to her face, inhaling its perfume. John Norman, she thought. John Norman.

The Speedway—now the Freeway—were already on stage; they were playing as her backup. Esther waited for her introduction. "Ladies and gentlemen, here's a friend of ours," called Lee Dallas.

Then, carrying the rose in her long fingers, she walked out on the stage, to the applause of more than twenty thousand people.

The audience, cheering and screaming, saw a slim girl with golden hair. She was dressed all in white, a white satin trouser suit that glimmered under the lights and made its own kind of light show around her. The girl didn't smile, but neither was she crying. Her face was calm, a little sad. She stood center stage, silent, still, waiting for the clapping and yelling to subside. When the audience was quiet, and she had their full attention, she spoke.

"I am Esther Hoffman Howard," she said.

As one, the audience rose to its feet, and every person in the house held up a lighted match. Esther looked out on the sea of flickering flames and felt a closeness with these people she had never before experienced. It was a kinship—a feeling of owing them something that she had to repay, a feeling that they owed something to her, and even more to John Norman. They weren't the enemy, after all.

Taking the microphone in her hand, she began to sing. It was a song new to the crowd, and they settled to listen. She sang "With One More Look at You," the song that John Norman had left behind him, the last song he'd ever written.

With one more look at you
I could learn to tame the clouds
And let the sun shine through
Leave a troubled past and I might start anew
I'll solve the mysteries if you're the prize
Refresh these tired eyes

With one more look at you
I might overcome the anger
That I've learned to know

Find a peace of mind I lost so long ago
Your gentle touch has made me strong again
And I belong again

For when you look at me
I'm everything and more that I had dreamed I'd be
My spirit feels a promise
I won't be alone
We'll love and live more
Love and live forever

With one more look at you
I'd learn to change the stars
And change our fortunes too
I'd have the constellations paint your portrait too
So all the world might share this wondrous sight
The world could end each night
With one more look at you
With one more look at you
I want one more look at you

When she finished it, she knew she had a hit. No, she and John Norman had a hit, because that's the way it was going to be. Without hesitation, she began to sing again.

For the first few bars, the Speedway faltered a little, caught off base. This wasn't the song they'd expected. But they knew it well, very well. It was their old theme song, "Watch Closely Now." Quickly, they moved into the backup, altering their key and their tempo to suit Esther's version, which was torchy, a ballad.

Can you hear me, Johnny? I'm singing *your* song, but it's mine now. You gave it to me. You gave me so much, Johnny, so much more than I had imagined. You're not dead, you're with me. You're inside me and with me forever. You're part of me always, as long as I'm alive, you're alive. And I'm gonna live a long time, Johnny, a long time. And I'm gonna sing your songs as well as my own, because you and I are one person, now and forever. How does it feel to be alive, Johnny?

Those closest to Esther, in the front rows, those who could see her face, would still be talking about it years later. How happy she looked suddenly, how filled with life and pleasure. How she threw back her head and without warning, belted the song out, made it a rocker. How she sang it as John Norman himself had sung it, so many times before he died.

In the years to come, they would remember how Esther Hoffman Howard had smiled.